NELSON

Math

GRADE 2

NELSON

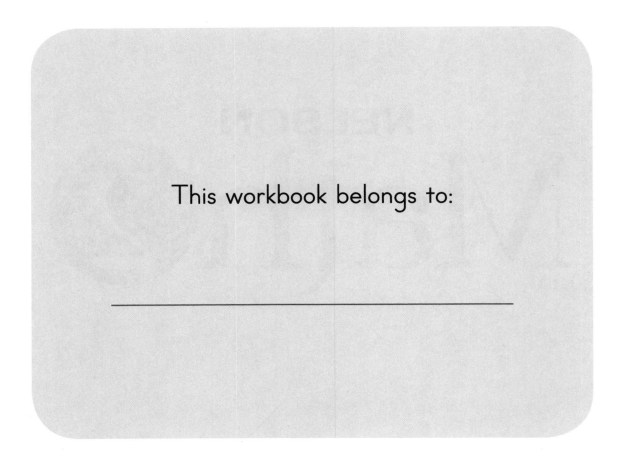

This workbook belongs to:

_____

NELSON

COPYRIGHT © 2018 by Nelson Education Ltd.

ISBN-13: 978-0-17-684828-6
ISBN-10: 0-17-684828-2

Printed and bound in Canada
1 2 3 4   21 20 19 18

For more information contact Nelson Education Ltd.,
1120 Birchmount Road, Toronto, Ontario M1K 5G4. Or you can
visit our website at nelson.com.

Cover Image
KidStock/Blend Images/Getty Images

Credits: Page iv: (clock) Panimoni/Shutterstock.com, (dice) igorrita/
Shutterstock.com, (pencil) Kolesov Sergei/Shutterstock.com,
(mathematical signs) OLEKSANDR TRETIACHENKO/Shutterstock.
com, (dominoes) sardez/Shutterstock.com, (yellow ruler) Rvector/
Shutterstock.com; 6: Mega Pixel/Shutterstock.com; 40: (butterfly)
suns07butterfly/Shutterstock.com, (ladybug) Ale-ks/iStock/Thinkstock;
46: (pencil) studiovin/Shutterstock.com, (toy car) Dan Kosmayer/
Shutterstock.com, (gluestick) Nor Gal/Shutterstock.com; 48:
(grasshopper) guy42/Shutterstock.com, (stamp) © Canada Post, Photo:
spatuletail/Shutterstock.com, (scissors) Vladvm/Shutterstock.com; 58:
(key) Feng Yu/Shutterstock.com, (battery) grey_and/Shutterstock.com;
61: (deer crossing sign) jojoo64/iStock/Thinkstock, (stop sign) FMStox/
Shutterstock.com, (school crossing sign) Christophe Testi/Shutterstock.
com; 78: (blue mug) ramzihachicho/iStock/Thinkstock, (milk jug)
Dimedrol68/Shutterstock.com, (measuring cup) Dancestrokes/
Shutterstock.com, (bucket) Andrey Eremin/Shutterstock.com, (egg
cup) WestLight/iStock/Thinkstock

Page 13, 19, 38, 88, 97: Coin images © 2018 Royal Canadian Mint. All
rights reserved / Images des pieces © 2018 Monnaie royale canadienne.
Tous droits réservés. (nickel) Photo: Pete Spiro/Shutterstock.com, (dime)
Photo: maogg/iStock, (quarter caribou side) Photo: maogg/iStock,
(quarter Queen side) Fat Jackey/Shutterstock.com, (loonie) Photo:
peterspiro/iStock, (toonie) Photo: maogg/iStock

Contents

REWARD CONTRACT

When you complete a topic in your
Nelson Math Workbook, colour in a circle.

START

Numbers

Number
Operations

Measurement

3-D Geometry
and 3-D
Measurement

2-D Geometry

Patterns

Data Management
and Probability

FINISH

Name: _____ Date: _____

My reward will be: _____

Parent/Guardian: _____

Reading and Writing Numbers

1. Match each number to its word.

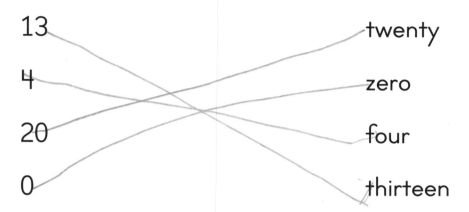

13   twenty

4   zero

20   four

0   thirteen

2. Write each word as a number.

three ___3___   fifteen ___15___

seven ___7___   eighteen ___18___

3. Write each number as a word.

11 _eleven_

14 _fourtine_

10 _ten_

12 _twelve_

LEARNING TIPS

Numbers can be written using numerals (for example, 16) or words (for example, sixteen). You may choose to use the word "number" when talking about numerals, as in the activities above.

Counting Forward

1. Count forward on the 100-chart.

Fill in the missing numbers.

1	2	3	4	5	6	7	8	9	10
11	12	13	14	15	16	17	18	19	20
21	22	23	24	25	26	27	28	29	30
31	32	33	34	35	36	37	38	39	40
41	42	43	44	45	46	47	48	49	50
51	52	53	54	55	56	57	58	59	60
61	62	63	64	65	66	67	68	69	70
71	72	73	74	75	76	77	78	79	80
81	82	83	84	85	86	87	88	89	90
91	92	93	94	95	96	97	98	99	100

2. Use the 100-chart from Question 1. Start at 50 and count forward by 2s. (Circle) each number in your counting pattern.

Now, start at 5. Count forward by 5s. Colour each number in your counting pattern yellow.

3. Write the missing numbers on the number lines.

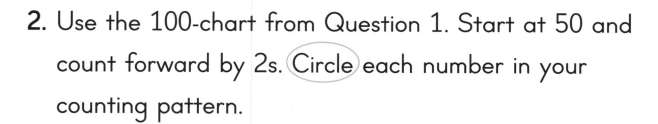

30   40   50   60   70   80   90   100

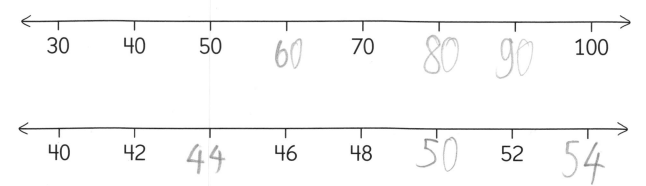

40   42   44   46   48   50   52   54

4. Write the missing numbers.

82, 83, 84, __85__, 86, __87__, __88__

34, 36, 38, __40__, __42__, 44, __46__

60, 65, 70, __75__, 80, __85__, __90__

19, 21, 23, __25__, __27__, 29, __31__

Counting Backward

LEARNING TIPS

A 100-chart can be used to help count forward or backward.

1. Start at 100. Count backward on the 100-chart. Fill in the missing numbers.

1	2	3	4	5	6	7	8	9	10
11	12	13	14	15	16	17	18	19	20
21	22	23	24	25	26	27	28	29	30
31	32	33	34	35	36	37	38	39	40
41	42	43	44	45	46	47	48	49	50
51	52	53	54	55	56	57	58	59	60
61	62	63	64	65	66	67	68	69	70
71	72	72	74	75	76	77	78	79	80
8	82	83	84	85	86	87	88	89	90
91	92	93	94	95	96	97	98	99	100

2. Write the missing numbers.

19, 18, 17, _16_, 15, _14_, _13_

40, 39, _38_, _37_, 36, _35_, 34

100, 90, _80_, _70_, 60, _50_, 40

3. Use the 100-chart from Question 1. Start at 96. Colour it red. Count backward by 10. Colour the square red. Continue to count backward by 10s. Colour the squares red.

What pattern do you notice?

_____

_____

4. Use the pattern you found in Question 3. Count backward by 10s from 91. Write the numbers.

_____

_____

Representing Numbers

1. (Circle) groups of 10 buttons.

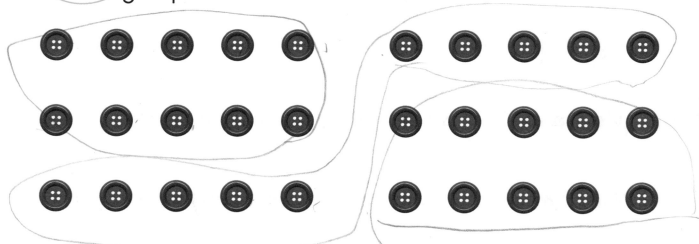

There are ___3___ groups of 10 buttons.

2. Write the number shown by the base ten blocks.

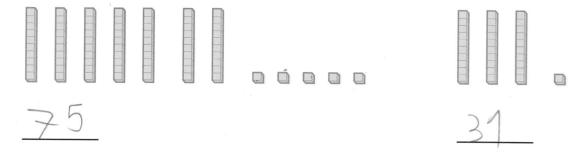

___75___   ___31___

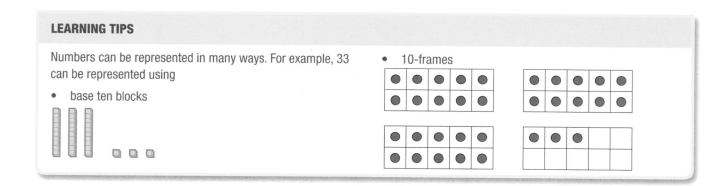

3. Write the number shown in each set of 10-frames.

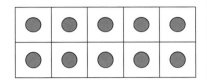 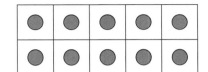 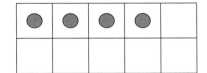

_24_

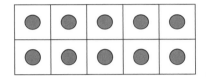 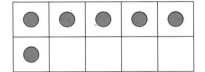

_16_

4. Draw dots on the 10-frames to represent each number.

28

 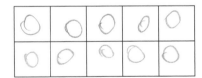 

47

Renaming Numbers

1. Write the number of tens and the number of ones.

94 = _____ tens and _____ ones

28 = _____ tens and _____ ones

2. Write the number.

7 tens and 6 ones = _____

3 tens and 9 ones = _____

2 tens and 4 ones = _____

3. Look at the base ten blocks.
Write the number in two ways.

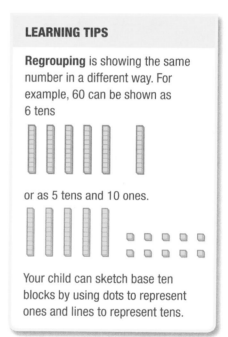

_____ tens and _____ ones = _____

_____ tens and _____ ones = _____

4. Write the number for each group of base ten blocks.

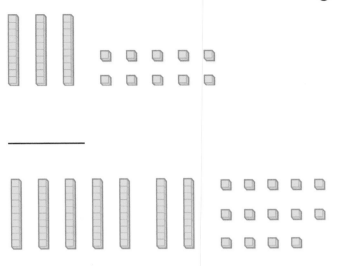

_____

_____

5. Write the number for each group of base ten blocks. **Regroup** the blocks. Draw a different set of base ten blocks to represent the same number.

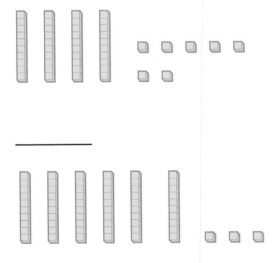

_____

_____

Comparing and Ordering Numbers

1. Circle the number that is greater. To help you, draw base ten blocks.

32	41
52	29
14	19

2. Circle the number that is less. To help you, draw base ten blocks.

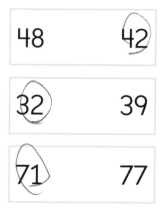

48	42
32	39
71	77

LEARNING TIPS

To compare 2-digit numbers, look at the tens first. The number with more tens is greater. If the number of tens is the same, then compare the ones.

3. Mark each pair of numbers on the number line.
Circle the number that is greater.

25   (33)

0   10   20   25 30 33   40   50

(58)   21

20 21   30   40   50   58 60   70

66   82

50   60   70   80   90   100

4. Order each set of numbers from least to greatest.
You can use the number lines above to help.

46, 78, 31 _____, _____, _____

61, 59, 56 _____, _____, _____

33, 69, 42 _____, _____, _____

Rounding 2-Digit Numbers

1. Look at the blue number. Circle the nearest ten.

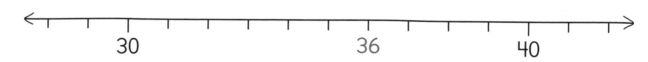

2. Round each number to the nearest ten.

84 _____   7 _____

13 _____   68 _____

35 _____   52 _____

LEARNING TIPS

One way to find the nearest ten is to draw a number line. For example, to find the nearest ten to 54, this number line can help.

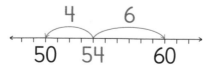

54 is 4 units from 50 and 6 units from 60, so 50 is the nearest ten.

For numbers with 5 in the ones digit, like 35, always round up to the nearest ten.

Counting Money

1. Name and write the value for each coin.

_____

_____5_____ ¢

_____

_____10_____ ¢

_____

_____25_____ ¢

_____

$ _1_

_____

$ _2_

2. Write the total value of the coins.

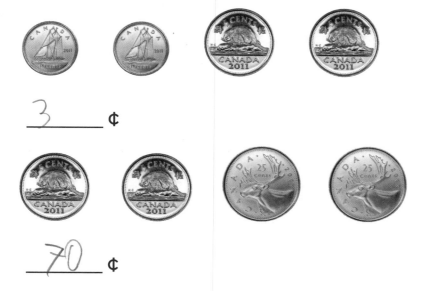

__3__ ¢

__70__ ¢

LEARNING TIPS

To count the value of coins, first add coins of the greatest value. Then skip count by 5s and 10s for remaining nickels and dimes.

Representing Fractions

1. Colour one half of each shape.

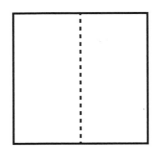 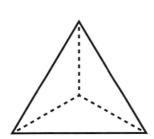 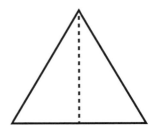

2. Colour one third of each shape.

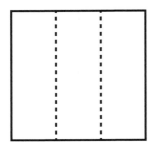 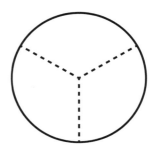

3. Colour one fourth of each shape.

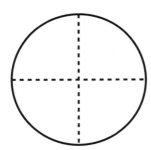 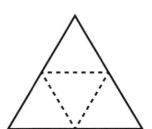 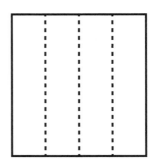

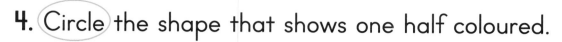

4. (Circle) the shape that shows one half coloured.

5. (Circle) the shape that shows one third coloured.

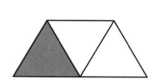
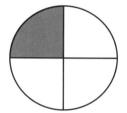
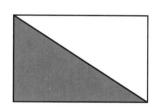

6. Match each shape to the fraction that shows how much
of the shape is coloured.

$\dfrac{1}{4}$

$\dfrac{1}{3}$

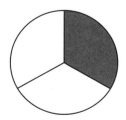
$\dfrac{1}{2}$

Comparing Fractions

1. (Circle) the fraction that shows how much of each shape is coloured.

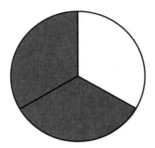

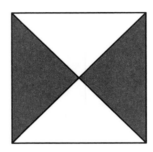

$\dfrac{1}{3}$ $\dfrac{2}{3}$

$\dfrac{1}{4}$ $\dfrac{2}{4}$

$\dfrac{3}{5}$ $\dfrac{4}{5}$

2. (Circle) the measuring cup that has more water.

   or

$\dfrac{1}{2}$ $\dfrac{1}{3}$

   or

$\dfrac{3}{4}$ $\dfrac{1}{2}$

LEARNING TIPS

$\dfrac{2}{4}$ of the square is red.

The 2 tells how many parts are red. The 4 tells how many equal parts there are.

3. Circle the pie that has more left over.

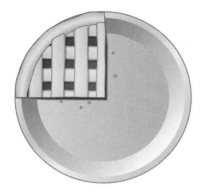   or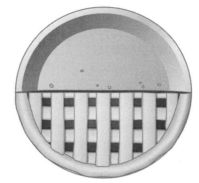

$\frac{1}{4}$ $\frac{1}{2}$

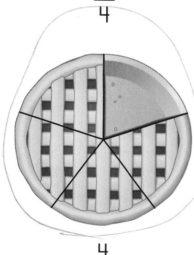   or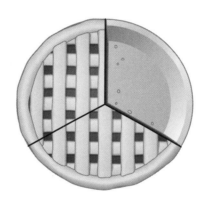

$\frac{4}{5}$ $\frac{2}{3}$

4. Circle the greater fraction.

$\frac{2}{5}$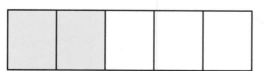

$\frac{2}{4}$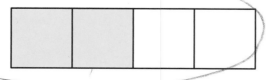

Test Yourself

1. Write the number for each word.

   eleven _____   eighteen _____

   nine _____   twelve _____

2. Write the missing numbers.

   12, 14, 16, _____, _____, 22, 24, _____

   25, 30, 35, _____, 45, _____, _____, 60

   40, 39, 38, _____, 36, _____, _____, 33

3. Write the number shown by the base ten blocks.

   _____

4. Write the number.

   4 tens and 9 ones = _____

   2 tens and 13 ones = _____

5. Circle the number that is greater.

42   or   24   78   or   87

6. Order these numbers from least to greatest: 94, 23, 74, 11

_____, _____, _____, _____

7. Round each number to the nearest ten.

62 _____   27 _____

8. Write the total value of the coins.

_____ ¢

9. Circle the shape that shows one third coloured.

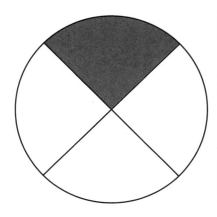 

Addition Strategies

1. Use counters on the 10-frames to add.

$7 + 4 =$ _____ $9 + 8 =$ _____

$8 + 5 =$ _____ $5 + 7 =$ _____

$8 + 6 =$ _____ $7 + 8 =$ _____

$6 + 7 =$ _____ $3 + 9 =$ _____

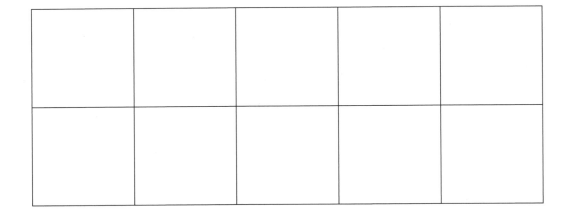

2. Add.

$1 + 1 =$ _____

$3 + 3 =$ _____

$7 + 7 =$ _____

$9 + 9 =$ _____

$5 + 5 =$ _____

$6 + 6 =$ _____

$4 + 4 =$ _____

$8 + 8 =$ _____

3. Add. Use **doubles** to help you.

$3 + 2 =$ _____

$4 + 5 =$ _____

$4 + 3 =$ _____

$8 + 7 =$ _____

$2 + 1 =$ _____

$6 + 7 =$ _____

$8 + 9 =$ _____

$6 + 5 =$ _____

LEARNING TIPS

Making 10 can help with addition. Combine two numbers to make 10, and then think about the extras. For example, to add $8 + 3$, think "$8 + 2$ is 10, and 1 more is 11."

When a number is added to itself, it's called a **double**. When two numbers are close to each other, think of a double to help add. Then add or subtract 1. For example, to add $5 + 6$, think of $5 + 5 + 1$ or $6 + 6 - 1$.

Reordering Numbers to Add

1. Complete each addition sentence.

$3 + 1 =$ _____, so $1 + 3 =$ _____

$4 + 5 =$ _____, so $5 + 4 =$ _____

$2 + 4 =$ _____, so $4 + 2 =$ _____

LEARNING TIPS

In an addition sentence, writing the numbers in a different order can help with adding. For example, to add $9 + 7 + 1$, think of $9 + 1 + 7$. First add $9 + 1$, which is 10, then add $10 + 7$, which is 17.

2. Change the order of the numbers to help you add them. Then add.

$9 + 5 + 1 =$ _____ + _____ + _____

$=$ _____ + _____

$=$ _____

$5 + 3 + 5 =$ _____ + _____ + _____

$=$ _____ + _____

$=$ _____

$8 + 7 + 2 =$ _____ + _____ + _____

$=$ _____ + _____

$=$ _____

Subtraction Strategies

1. Subtract. Think about a number line to help you.

$5 - 2 =$ _____ $12 - 9 =$ _____

$8 - 4 =$ _____ $18 - 14 =$ _____

$9 - 3 =$ _____ $15 - 11 =$ _____

2. Subtract. Think about addition to help you.

$15 - 8 =$ _____ $8 - 3 =$ _____

$12 - 6 =$ _____ $18 - 9 =$ _____

$10 - 4 =$ _____ $11 - 5 =$ _____

3. Subtract.

$8 - 7 =$ _____ $6 - 5 =$ _____

$9 - 9 =$ _____ $6 - 6 =$ _____

$5 - 4 =$ _____ $9 - 8 =$ _____

LEARNING TIPS

When subtracting numbers that are close together, think about the hops between them on a number line. For example, to subtract $12 - 8$, think, "How many hops are between 8 and 12?"

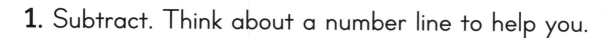

There are 4 hops between 8 and 12, so $12 - 8 = 4$

Exploring Zero

1. How many balls are there altogether?

 +

0 + 9 = _____

 −

7 − 0 = _7___

2. Add or subtract.

21 + 0 = _21___   17 + 0 = _17___

0 + 21 = _21___   0 + 17 = _17___

21 − 0 = _21___   17 − 0 = _17___

LEARNING TIPS

When you add zero to a number, the number does not change because you are adding nothing. When you subtract 0 from a number, the number doesn't change because you are taking away nothing.

Comparison Problems

Write an addition or a subtraction sentence for each question.

1. How many more green balls are there than orange balls?

_____

There are _____ more green balls than orange balls.

2. There are 12 children on the red team and 9 children on the blue team. How many more children are on the red team?

_____

_____

LEARNING TIPS

You can add or subtract to compare numbers. For example, if there are 3 cats and 5 dogs, to find out how many more dogs there are, you can:

- add: $3 + \boxed{} = 5$
  $3 + 2 = 5$, so there are 2 more dogs
- or subtract: $5 - 3 = 2$, so there are 2 more dogs

Fact Families

Make a **fact family** for each number.

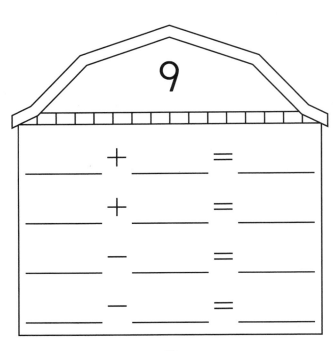

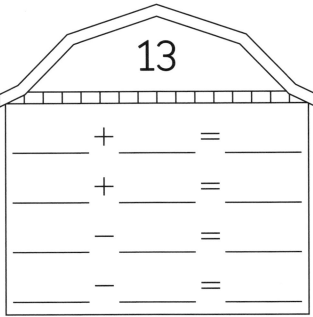

Missing-Part Addition and Subtraction

1. Balance each scale. Add or cross out balls on the left side.

Then complete the addition or subtraction sentence.

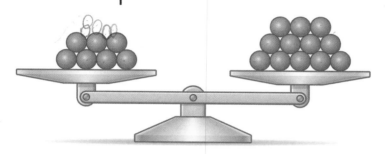

7 + ___5___ = 12

LEARNING TIPS

To find missing numbers in a subtraction sentence (such as 14 – ☐ = 9), think about the related addition fact. 9 + 5 = 14, so the missing part is 5.

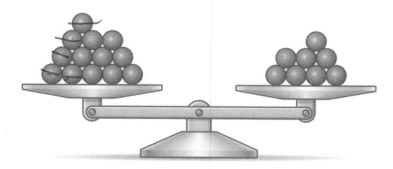

13 – ___5___ = 8

2. Determine the missing number.

8 + ___9___ = 17

___5___ + 10 = 15

14 – ___6___ = 8

___18___ – 3 = 15

Relating Equal Groups

1. Balance each scale. Draw linking cubes on one side.

2. Fill in the blanks. Each addition sentence should have equal value on both sides.

$2 + 6 = 4 + \underline{4}$

$4 + 5 = 8 + \underline{1}$

$9 + 7 = \underline{10} + 6$

$3 + 8 = \underline{11} + \underline{0}$

$6 + 9 = \underline{14} + \underline{0}$

$8 + 3 = \underline{11} + \underline{0}$

$5 + 12 = \underline{17} + \underline{0}$

LEARNING TIPS

The equal sign (=) means that what is on the left side and what is on the right side are the same. For example, 2 + 2 = 4, and 2 + 2 = 1 + 3 because both sides have a value of 4.

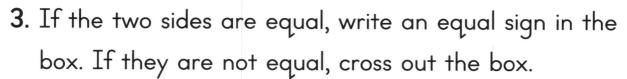

Goal: I can add different pairs of numbers to get the same value.

3. If the two sides are equal, write an equal sign in the box. If they are not equal, cross out the box.

7 + 9 ☐(=) 6 + 10

5 + 5 ☐(≠) 6 + 3
10

11 + 6 ☐(=) 8 + 9
17

3 + 12 ☐(≠) 6 + 8
15

13 + 5 ☐(=) 9 + 9
18

4. Write 2 different addition expressions that equal the number given.

10 = _____ + _____ = _____ + _____

12 = _____ + _____ = _____ + _____

9 = _____ + _____ = _____ + _____

14 = _____ + _____ = _____ + _____

16 = _____ + _____ = _____ + _____

Adding 2-Digit Numbers

1. Add.

20 + 20 = _____   20 + 40 = _____

30 + 50 = _____   80 + 20 = _____

40 + 30 = _____   30 + 10 = _____

2. Add.

35 + 10 = _____   44 + 10 = _____

18 + 10 = _____   67 + 10 = _____

22 + 10 = _____   56 + 10 = _____

3. Separate the tens and ones for each number.

22 = 20 + _____   34 = 30 + _____

76 = _____ + 6   81 = _____ + 1

55 = 50 + _____   99 = _____ + 9

LEARNING TIPS

When adding 2-digit numbers, separate the tens and ones, and add them separately. For example, to add 23 + 51, think of it as 20 + 50 = 70 and 3 + 1 = 4. Then add the sums: 70 + 4 = 74.

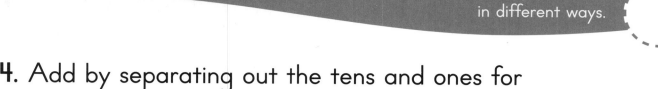

4. Add by separating out the tens and ones for both numbers.

26 + 11   43 + 35

5. Add. Draw base ten blocks in the place-value chart to help you.

22 + 56

Tens	Ones

```
    2   2
+   5   6
_____
```

Adding with Regrouping

1. Regroup to add.

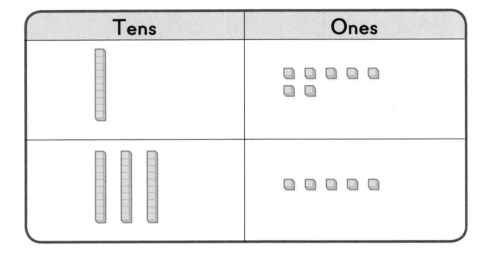

Tens	Ones

$$\begin{array}{r} 17 \\ + 35 \\ \hline \end{array}$$

Tens	Ones

$$\begin{array}{r} 36 \\ + 29 \\ \hline \end{array}$$

LEARNING TIPS

To regroup when adding, trade 10 ones blocks for 1 tens block.

2. Show how to add 44 + 28. Draw base ten blocks on
   the place value chart. Then add.

Tens	Ones

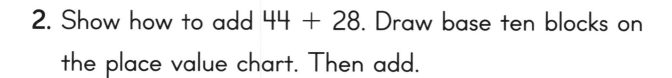

3. Regroup to add.

$\overset{1}{6}6$
$+\ 18$
$8\ 4$

$\overset{1}{2}8$
$+\ 38$
$6\ 6$

$\overset{1}{2}6$
$+\ 14$
$4\ 0$

$\overset{1}{6}4$
$+\ 27$
$9\ 1$

$\overset{1}{3}4$
$+\ 59$
$9\ 3$

$\overset{1}{2}5$
$+\ 47$
$7\ 2$

Subtracting with 2-Digit Numbers

1. Subtract.

90 − 30 = _____   64 − 10 = _____

50 − 20 = _____   37 − 10 = _____

73 − 30 = _____   45 − 20 = _____

2. Subtract. Use a number line to help you.

27 − 9 = _____

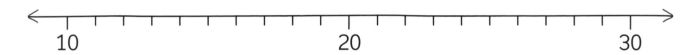

42 − 4 = _____

LEARNING TIPS

When using a number line to subtract, count backward on the number line.
When using base ten blocks to subtract, cross out the blocks being subtracted.

3. Subtract. Cross out the blocks that are being subtracted.

45 − 23 = _____

68 − 35 = _____

77 − 32 = _____

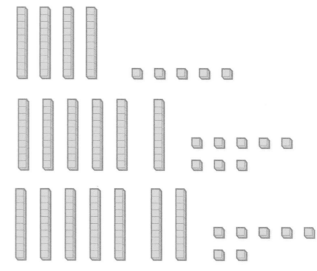

4. Subtract. Draw base ten blocks to help you.

44 − 13 = _____   25 − 15 = _____

56 − 32 = _____   99 − 18 = _____

Subtracting with Regrouping

1. Subtract. Regroup 1 ten for 10 ones. Use the place value charts to help you.

$$\begin{array}{r} 55 \\ -7 \\ \hline \end{array}$$

Tens	Ones

$$\begin{array}{r} 46 \\ -8 \\ \hline \end{array}$$

Tens	Ones

$$\begin{array}{r} 60 \\ -25 \\ \hline \end{array}$$

Tens	Ones

LEARNING TIPS

To regroup when subtracting, trade 1 tens block for 10 ones blocks. For example, to subtract 42 – 8, think of 42 as 3 tens and 12 ones. Then you can subtract 8 ones from 12 ones.

2. Subtract by regrouping.

```
  65
-  7
-----
```

_____ tens   _____ ones

—   _____ ones
_____

_____ tens   _____ ones

```
  43
-  6
-----
```

_____ tens   _____ ones

—   _____ ones
_____

_____ tens   _____ ones

3. Subtract.

```
  42          51          64
- 13        - 33        - 28
-----       -----       -----
```

```
  23          72          45
- 18        - 44        - 26
-----       -----       -----
```

Adding and Subtracting with Money

1. Is there enough money to buy each item? Write how much money there is. (Circle) the answer.

_____ ¢

Yes   or   No

_____ ¢

Yes   or   No

2. Add.

55¢	45¢	60¢
+ 10¢	+ 35¢	+ 15¢
¢	¢	¢

3. Subtract.

50¢	85¢	45¢
— 35¢	— 30¢	— 25¢
___	___	___
¢	¢	¢

4. Circle two items you can buy together if you have 75¢.
Show your addition.

How much do you have left? Show your subtraction.

Exploring Multiplication

1. Write an addition sentence for each picture.

Then write a multiplication sentence.

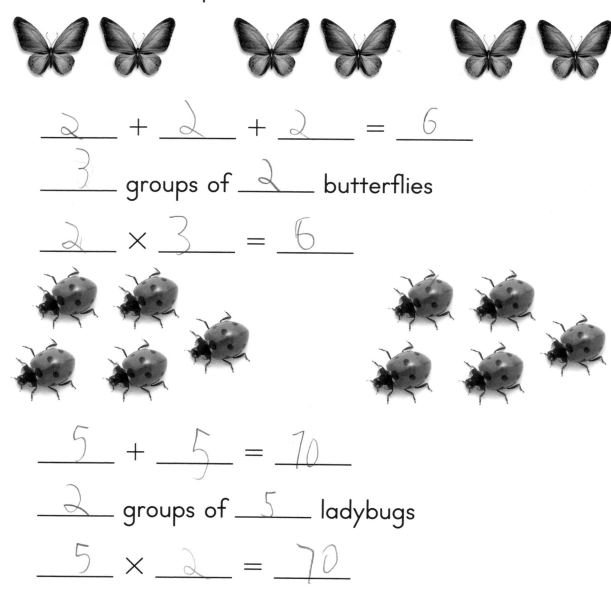

__2__ + __2__ + __2__ = __6__

__3__ groups of __2__ butterflies

__2__ × __3__ = __6__

__5__ + __5__ = __10__

__2__ groups of __5__ ladybugs

__5__ × __2__ = __10__

> **LEARNING TIPS**
>
> You **multiply** when you join equal groups. For example, 2 + 2 + 2 + 2 can be written as 4 × 2. This means the total of 4 groups of 2. So, 4 × 2 = 8.

2. Write each addition sentence as a multiplication sentence. Then **multiply**.

$3 + 3 + 3 + 3 + 3 =$ __15__

__5__ $\times$ __3__ $=$ __15__

$4 + 4 =$ __8__

__2__ $\times$ __4__ $=$ __8__

$2 + 2 + 2 + 2 =$ __8__

__2__ $\times$ __4__ $=$ __8__

3. Multiply. Draw a picture to help you.

$2 \times 2 =$ __4__

$1 \times 7 =$ __7__

Exploring Division

LEARNING TIPS

To **divide** means to separate a collection into equal groups or shares. For example, to share 6 stickers between 2 people, each person gets 3 stickers.

1. You have 8 jelly beans for 2 people to share.

Show how you can share the jelly beans equally.

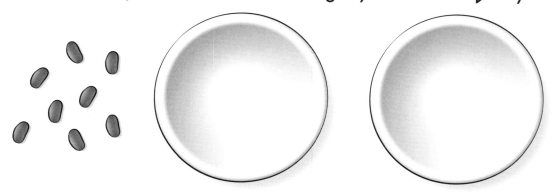

Complete the division sentence: 8 ÷ 2 = _____

Each person gets _____ jelly beans.

2. You have 6 pears for 3 people to share.

Show how you can share the pears equally.

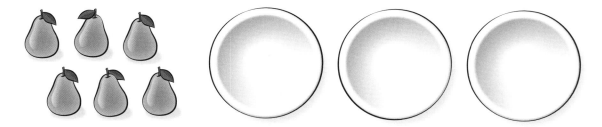

Complete the division sentence: 6 ÷ 3 = _____

Each person gets _____ pears.

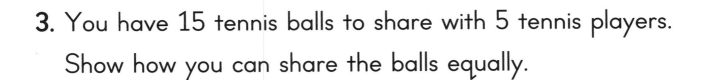

3. You have 15 tennis balls to share with 5 tennis players. Show how you can share the balls equally.

Complete the division sentence.

15 ÷ _____ = _____

Each tennis player gets _____ tennis balls.

4. Divide. You can draw a picture to help you.

4 ÷ 2 = _____   10 ÷ 2 = _____

9 ÷ 3 = _____   8 ÷ 4 = _____

Test Yourself

1. Add. Use doubles to help you.

6 + 5 = _____   8 + 7 = _____

2. Change the order of the numbers to make them easier to add. Then add.

8 + 5 + 2 = _____ + _____ + _____

= _____ + _____

= _____

3. Subtract.

11 − 6 = _____   16 − 8 = _____

4. Add or subtract.

17 + 0 = _____   14 − 0 = _____

5. Write the missing number.

6 + _____ = 15   15 − _____ = 11

6. Add or subtract.

$$56 + 24$$

$$66 - 32$$

$$72 - 14$$

7. Multiply. Draw a picture to help you.

$3 \times 4 =$ _____

$2 \times 5 =$ _____

8. You have 10 candies to share with 5 friends. Show how to share the candies equally.

Complete the division sentence.

$10 \div 5 =$ _____

Each friend gets _____ candies.

Measuring in Centimetres

1. Write the length in **centimetres (cm)**.

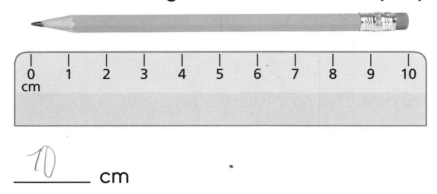

_____10_____ cm

2. Use a ruler to measure the length of each object.

_____7_____ cm

_____9_____ cm

LEARNING TIPS

A **centimetre** is a unit of measure. The symbol for a centimetre is **cm**. Remind your child to make sure one end of the object is lined up with 0 cm on the ruler.

Measuring in Metres

1. Use a measuring tape to measure each object to the nearest **metre (m)**.

the length of your bed: about _____ m

the length of a table: about _____ m

the length of a wall: about _____ m

the length of a hallway: about _____ m

2. Circle the most appropriate unit of measurement for each object.

the length of your school

cm   m

the length of your finger

cm   m

the length of a school bus

cm   m

LEARNING TIPS

A **metre** is a unit of measurement that is longer than a centimetre. The symbol for metres is **m**. 1 m = 100 cm.

If you do not have a metre stick or measuring tape in your home, your child can estimate measurements in metres.

Using Benchmarks to Estimate

1. Estimate the length in centimetres.

Then use a ruler to measure.

Estimate: about _____ cm

Estimate: about _____ cm

Measurement: _____ cm

Measurement: _____ cm

Estimate: about _____ cm

Measurement: _____ cm

2. Estimate the length in centimetres. Then use a ruler to measure.

length of this book

Estimate: about _____ cm   Measure: _____ cm

length of a fork

Estimate: about _____ cm   Measure: _____ cm

3. Estimate the length in metres. Then use a measuring tape to measure.

length of a rug

Estimate: about _____ m   Measure: _____ m

length of a hallway

Estimate: about _____ m   Measure: _____ m

LEARNING TIPS

It helps to use a personal reference to estimate lengths. The width of a child's fingertip is about 1 cm. A child's very large step is about 1 m.

Measuring Perimeter

1. Find the **perimeter** of each object.

Perimeter: _____ crayons

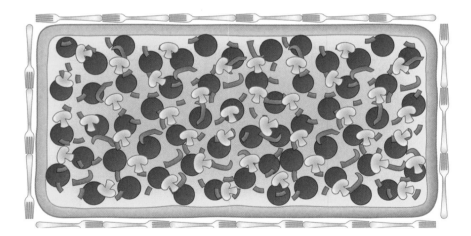

Perimeter: _____ forks

2. Place a separate piece of string along the perimeter of each shape. Start the string at the star. Cut each piece of string to match the perimeter of the shape.

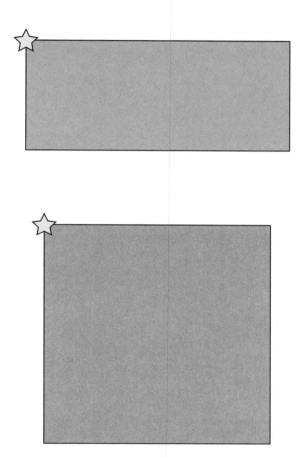

Compare the perimeter of the two shapes by comparing the two pieces of string. (Circle) the shape that has a greater perimeter.

Days, Weeks, Months, and Years

1. Write the days of the week in order starting from Sunday.

_____

_____

_____

2. How many days are there in 2 weeks?

_____ days

How many days are there in 3 weeks?

_____ days

3. Complete the table.

Month before	Month	Month after
	February	
	May	
	August	
	November	

4. Write these birth dates in order from earliest in the year to latest.

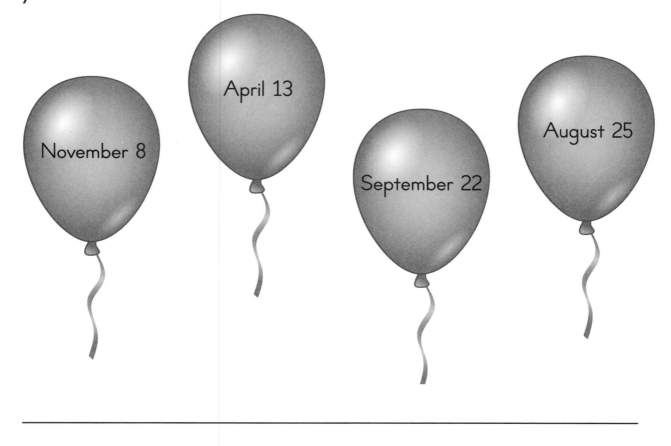

_____

_____

5. Ming is 20 months old. Her brother Chen is 3 years old. Who is older? Show your work.

_____

_____

LEARNING TIPS

There are 7 days in 1 week. Most months have 30 or 31 days. There are 12 months in a year.

Telling Time

1. Write each time using words.

quarter past   half past   _____

_____   _____   _____

2. Draw hands on the clock to show each time.

three o'clock   half past two   quarter to seven

LEARNING TIPS

Remind your child that the big hand shows minutes and the small hand shows hours. Help your child to think of time in quarters of an hour. For example, a quarter past means 15 minutes past a certain hour.

3. Match each clock to the correct time.

4:15   7:45   10:30

4. Write each time on the digital clock.

nine o'clock

twelve thirty

five fifteen

seven forty-five

Understanding Temperature

1. (Circle) the **thermometer** in each pair that shows a colder temperature.

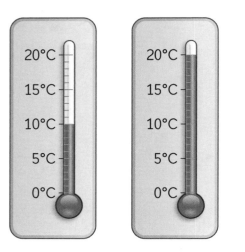 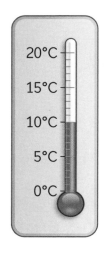 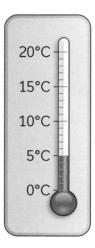

2. The thermometer on the left shows the temperature in the morning. In the afternoon it gets warmer. Colour the thermometer to show what it might look like.

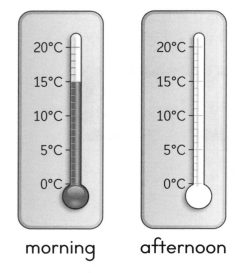

morning   afternoon

LEARNING TIPS

A **thermometer** tells temperature. When the temperature gets hotter, the red liquid goes up. When it gets colder, the liquid goes down.

3. Draw a (circle) around each item of clothing people might wear if the thermometer looks like this.

Test Yourself

1. Circle the most appropriate unit of measurement for each object.

    the height of a flag pole   cm   m

    the length of a book   cm   m

2. Estimate the length of each object in centimetres. Then measure to check your estimate.

    Estimate: about _____ cm

    Measurement: _____ cm

    Estimate: about _____ cm

    Measurement: _____ cm

3. Leah is 36 months old. Her brother Lucas is 2 years old. Who is older? Show your work.

    _____

    _____

4. Find the perimeter of the picture frame.

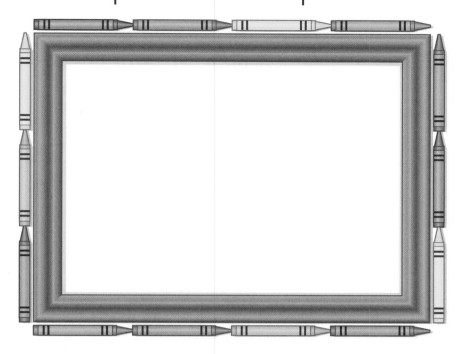

Perimeter: _____ crayons

5. Write the correct time on the digital clocks.

Identifying 2-D Shapes

1. Write the number of sides and number of **vertices** for each shape.

Shape	Number of sides	Number of vertices
triangle		
rectangle		
square		
pentagon		
hexagon		
octagon		

2. A **quadrilateral** has 4 sides. (Circle) the quadrilaterals.

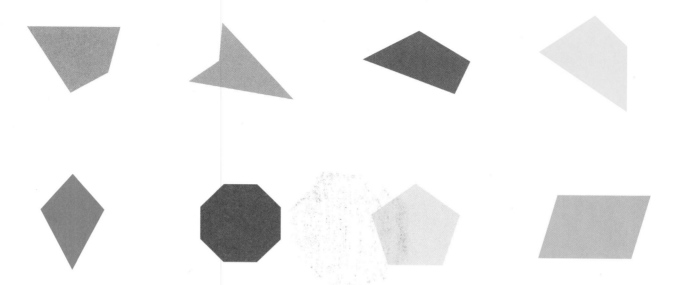

3. Match each street sign with its shape name.

octagon   pentagon   quadrilateral

Sorting 2-D Shapes

1. Colour the triangles red, the quadrilaterals blue, the pentagons orange, the hexagons green, and the octagons purple.

> **LEARNING TIPS**
>
> Triangles have 3 sides, quadrilaterals have 4 sides, pentagons have 5 sides, hexagons have 6 sides, and octagons have 8 sides.

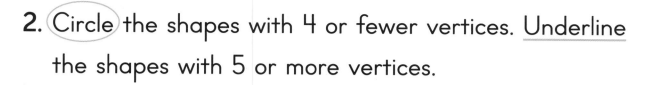

2. (Circle) the shapes with 4 or fewer vertices. <u>Underline</u> the shapes with 5 or more vertices.

triangle   pentagon   rectangle

hexagon   square   octagon

Draw these shapes on the correct grid.

Shapes with 4 or fewer vertices

Shapes with 5 or more vertices

Pictures Using 2-D Shapes

1. Name the shapes in this picture.

How many of each shape are there?

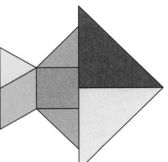

_____

_____

2. Create a picture using 2-D shapes. Draw it below.

Name the shapes in your picture.

_____

_____

Creating and Taking Apart 2-D Shapes

1. Create a square by drawing 2 triangles.

Create a rectangle by drawing 2 triangles.

2. Take apart the rectangles. Draw lines on each rectangle to make 4 new shapes.

Exploring Symmetry

1. (Circle) each shape that shows one **line of symmetry**.

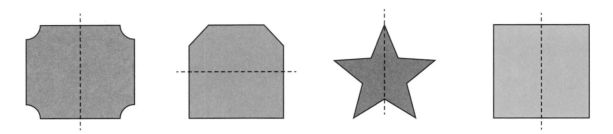

2. Draw at least one line of symmetry on each shape.

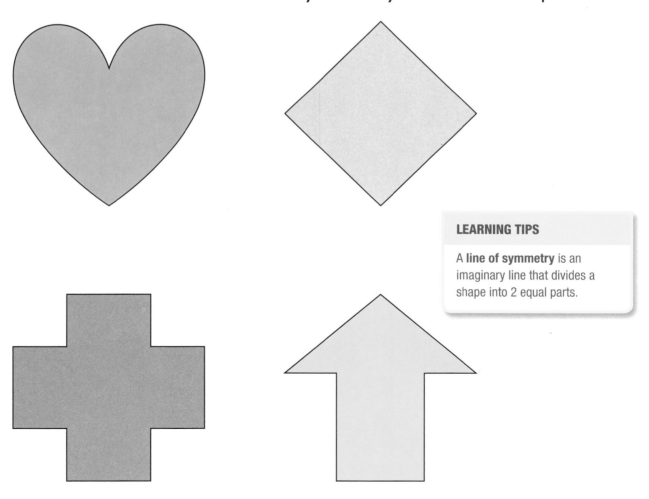

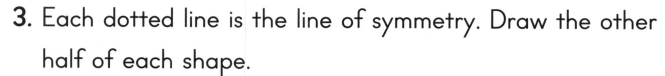

3. Each dotted line is the line of symmetry. Draw the other half of each shape.

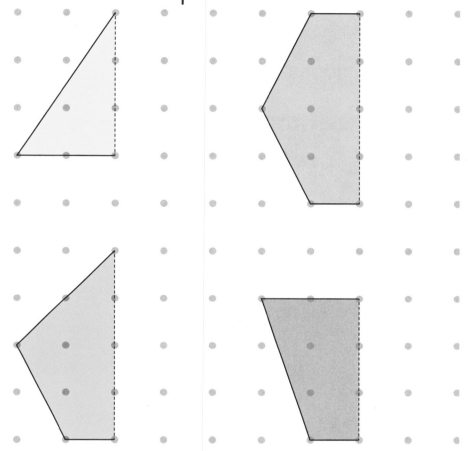

4. The picture should be symmetrical. Draw the missing parts.

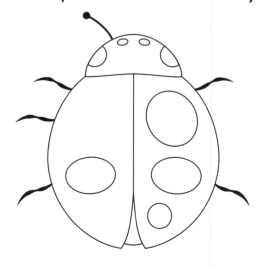

Objects on a Map

This is Eva's bedroom. Eva is standing in front of her bedroom door.

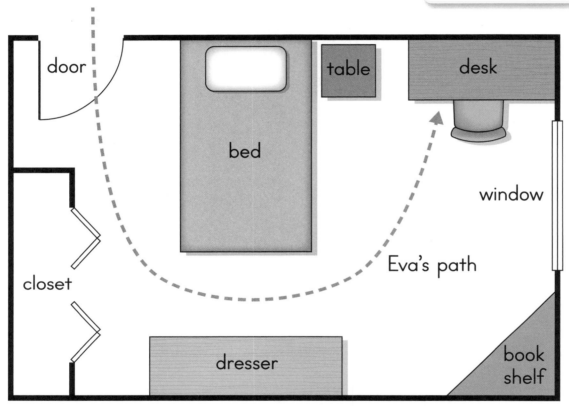

1. Describe the path Eva takes to her desk.

_____

_____

_____

_____

2. Circle the correct word to describe the positions of the objects in Eva's room.

The door is to the left / right of the bed

The desk is to the left / right of the table.

3. Draw a simple map of your own bedroom.

Exploring Area

1. Estimate the **area** of each rectangle. Then count the squares to determine the area.

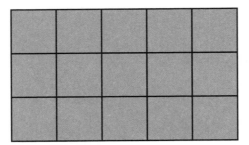

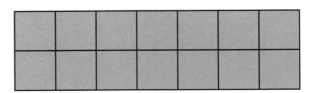

Estimate:

about _____ squares

Measure: _____ squares

Estimate:

about _____ squares

Measure: _____ squares

2. Determine the area of this quilt in two different ways.

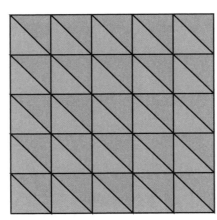

Area of quilt:

_____ squares

_____ triangles

LEARNING TIPS

Area is the amount of space covered by something. When recording an area measurement, write the number and the type of unit used.

Test Yourself

1. Complete the table.

Shape	Draw the shape	Number of sides
square		
triangle		
rectangle		

2. Draw at least one line of symmetry on each shape.

 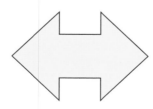 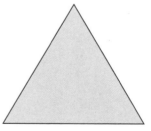

3. Determine the area of the rectangle.

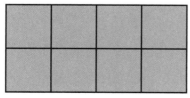

_____ squares

Identifying 3-D Objects

1. Match the 3-D object to its name.

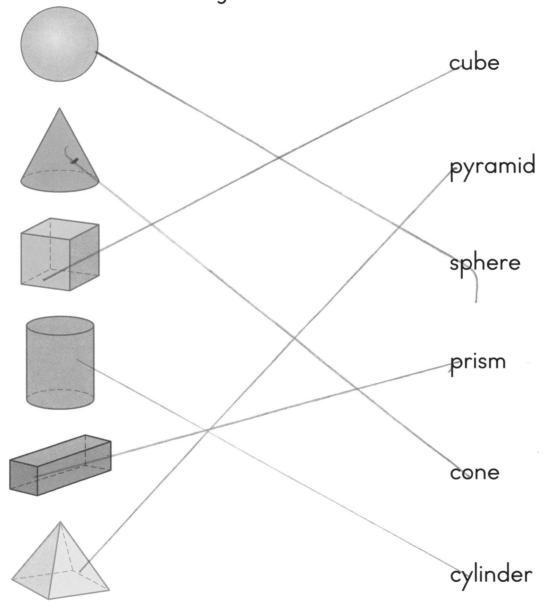

cube

pyramid

sphere

prism

cone

cylinder

2. What 3-D object does each item look like? Write the 3-D object.

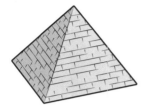

_____   _____   _____

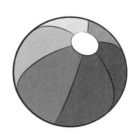

_____   _____   _____

3. What shape is at the ends of this prism?

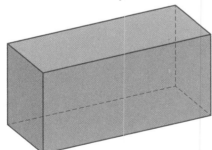

_____

What shape is at the ends of this prism?

_____

Sorting 3-D Objects

1. Sort the 3-D objects. Write their names in the table.

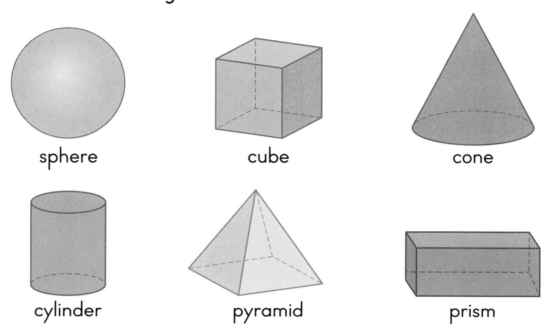

sphere   cube   cone

cylinder   pyramid   prism

Only flat faces	Some curved faces

LEARNING TIPS

The sides of a 3-D object are called **faces**.

2. Sort the 3-D objects. Write their names in the table.

cone

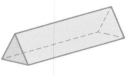
prism

pyramid

cylinder

Flat circular face(s)	Flat rectangular faces

3. Does each shape slide, stack, or roll?

Circle all the words that are correct.

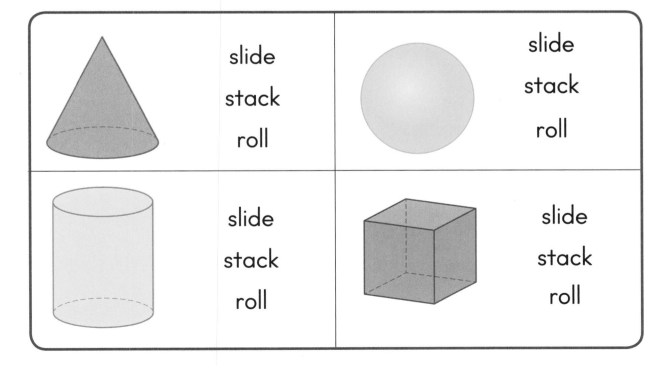

slide

stack

roll

slide

stack

roll

slide

stack

roll

slide

stack

roll

Modelling 3-D Objects

Build a **skeleton** of a cube and pyramid. Use toothpicks or straws for the **edges**. Use modelling clay or small marshmallows for the vertices.

How many vertices does the cube have?

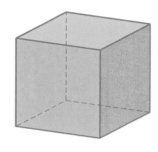

_____

How many edges does the cube have?

_____

How many vertices does the pyramid have?

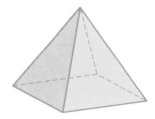

_____

How many edges does the pyramid have?

_____

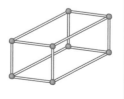

Exploring Mass

1. Circle the heavier object.

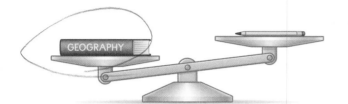

2. What is the mass of each object?

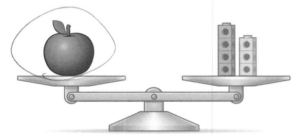
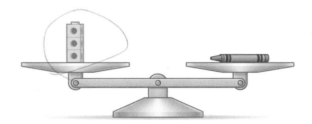

Apple: ___7___ cubes   Crayon: ___3___ cubes

3. Choose two objects in your home. Estimate which object has the greater mass. Draw the objects on the scale.

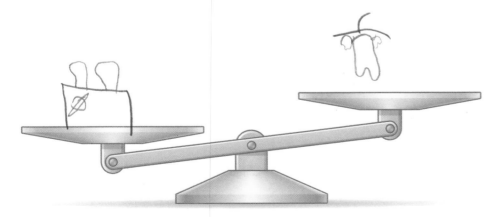

Exploring Capacity

1. (Circle) the container that has a greater **capacity**.

2. Order the containers from least to greatest capacity.

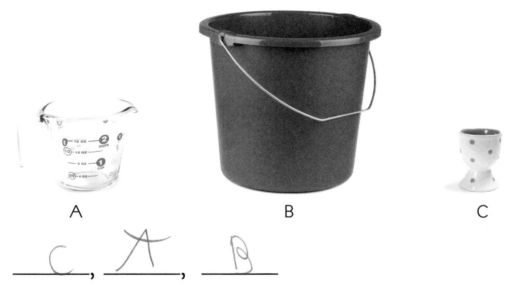

A   B   C

____C____, ____A____, ____B____

3. Measure the capacity of an object in your home. Count the number of glasses of water that will fill it.

Object: _____

Capacity: _____ glasses of water

Test Yourself

1. Look at the 3-D objects.

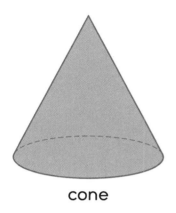

cone

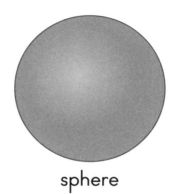

sphere

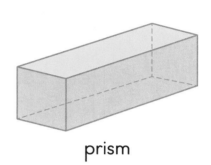

prism

Which object has a square face? _prism_

Which object has a circle face? _sphere_

Which object can roll but not slide? _____

Which object has the most vertices? _cone_

2. Circle the heavier object.

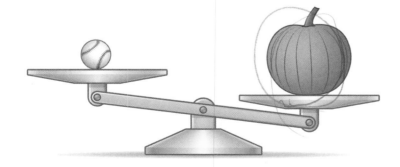

Repeating Patterns

1. Describe the **pattern core** for each pattern.

Pattern core: _____

_____

Pattern core: _____

_____

Pattern core: _____

_____

LEARNING TIPS

The **pattern core** is the part of a pattern that repeats.

---

2. Draw the missing picture for each pattern.

3. Draw a pattern with 2 colours and 2 shapes.

Describe the pattern.

_____

_____

_____

_____

Growing Patterns

1. Write a **pattern rule** for each **growing pattern**.

Then extend the pattern.

A, AA, AAA, <u>A</u>, <u>AA</u>

Pattern rule: _____

_____

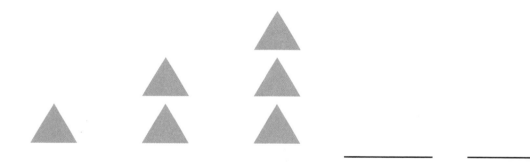

_____ _____

Pattern rule: _____

_____

LEARNING TIPS

Growing patterns increase in a regular way. **Pattern rules** describe a pattern. For example, the pattern rule for this growing pattern is start at 5 and add 5 each time: 5, 10, 15, 20, 25

2. Write the number you add for each growing pattern.
Then extend the pattern.

20, 22, 24, 26, 28, _____, _____, _____

Pattern rule: Add _____ each time

35, 40, 45, 50, 55, _____, _____, _____

Pattern rule: Add _____ each time

3. Is this a growing pattern? Explain why or why not.

2, 4, 6, 8, 10

_____

_____

Is this a growing pattern? Explain why or why not.

1, 2, 7, 10, 12

_____

_____

Shrinking Patterns

1. Write a pattern rule for each **shrinking pattern**.

Then extend the pattern.

Pattern rule: _____

_____

Pattern rule: _____

_____

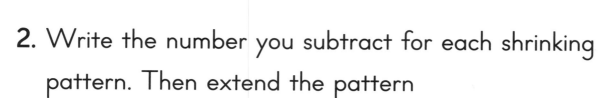

2. Write the number you subtract for each shrinking pattern. Then extend the pattern

19, 18, 17, 16, 15, _____, _____, _____

Pattern rule: Subtract _____ each time.

35, 30, 25, 20, 15, _____, _____, _____

Pattern rule: Subtract _____ each time.

3. Is this a shrinking pattern? Explain why or why not.

50, 40, 38, 20, 15

_____

_____

Is this a shrinking pattern? Explain why or why not.

20, 18, 16, 14, 12

_____

_____

Patterns in a 100-Chart

LEARNING TIPS

Your child can use the words "column" and "row" to help describe the pattern. Remind your child to remove the counters before starting a new pattern.

You will need small objects, such as buttons or dimes, to use as counters on the 100-chart.

column

row →

1	2	3	4	5	6	7	8	9	10
11	12	13	14	15	16	17	18	19	20
21	22	23	24	25	26	27	28	29	30
31	32	33	34	35	36	37	38	39	40
41	42	43	44	45	46	47	48	49	50
51	52	53	54	55	56	57	58	59	60
61	62	63	64	65	66	67	68	69	70
71	72	73	74	75	76	77	78	79	80
81	82	83	84	85	86	87	88	89	90
91	92	93	94	95	96	97	98	99	100

1. Place counters on the 100-chart to make each pattern. Describe how the counters look on the 100-chart.

   Start at 5. Skip count forward by 5s to 50.

   _____

   _____

   _____

   Start at 30. Skip count backward by 2s to 22.

   _____

   _____

   _____

2. What pattern do you notice on the 100-chart when skip counting by 2s?

   _____

   _____

   _____

Creating Patterns

1. Create a growing number pattern. Write the pattern rule.

   _____, _____, _____, _____, _____

   Pattern rule: Add _____ each time.

   Create a shrinking number pattern. Write the pattern rule.

   _____, _____, _____, _____, _____

   Pattern rule: Subtract _____ each time.

2. Draw 1 nickel. Create a growing pattern using more nickels.

LEARNING TIPS

In growing and shrinking patterns, numbers can change or the number of shapes or objects can change. For Question 2, encourage your child to first use actual nickels to show the pattern.

Test Yourself

1. Draw the missing picture for the pattern.

Write the pattern core.

_____

2. Write the number you add or subtract for each pattern. Then extend the pattern.

40, 50, 60, 70, _____, _____, _____

Pattern rule: Add _____ each time.

85, 80, 75, 70, 65, _____, _____, _____

Pattern rule: Subtract _____ each time.

3. Draw a shrinking pattern using dots.

Organizing Objects

1. Write the name or draw a picture of each object in the correct box.

	has 4 legs	does not have 4 legs
animal		
not an animal		

Conducting a Survey

Ask friends and family this **survey** question: What is your favourite day of the week? Use this tally chart to collect your data. Use one **tally mark** for each person's favourite.

Favourite day of the week	Tally
Sunday	
Monday	
Tuesday	
Wednesday	
Thursday	
Friday	
Saturday	

Circle the favourite day.

LEARNING TIPS

A **survey** is a question asked to find information. A **tally mark** is a way of keeping count by drawing marks. This is how tally marks appear to represent each number.

I	II	III	IIII	‖‖	‖‖ I	‖‖ II	‖‖ III	‖‖ IIII	‖‖ ‖‖
1	2	3	4	5	6	7	8	9	10

Pictographs

1. Look at the pictograph. Answer the questions below.

Favourite Colours in Lianne's Class

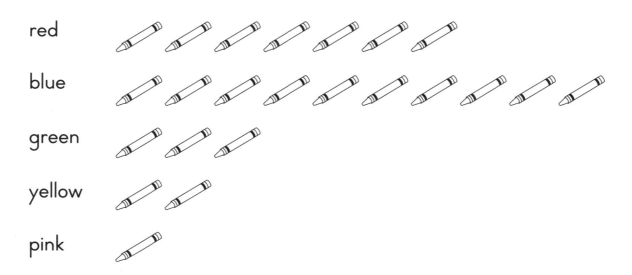

Each ✏ represents 1 person's choice.

What colour is the most favourite in Lianne's class?

_____

What colour is the least favourite in Lianne's class?

_____

> **LEARNING TIPS**
>
> A **pictograph** has symbols to show information. The symbol is the same in each column or row.

2. Use the data in the table below to create a pictograph.

Treats Sold at a Bake Sale	
cupcakes	5
cookies	7
brownies	3

Title: _____

cupcakes

cookies

brownies

Each ☐ represents 1 treat.

Which treat was sold the most?

_____

Data Management and Probability   93

Bar Graphs

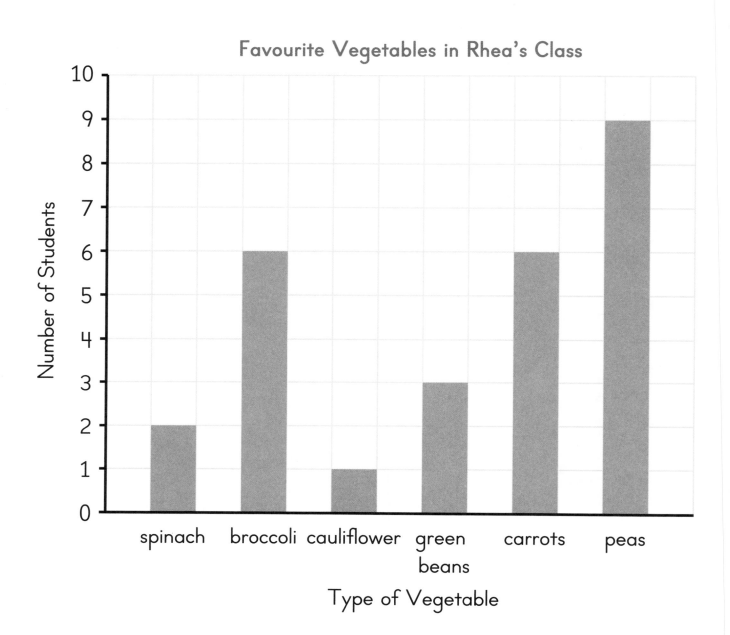

Favourite Vegetables in Rhea's Class

Number of Students (0–10) vs. Type of Vegetable: spinach 2, broccoli 6, cauliflower 1, green beans 3, carrots 6, peas 9.

LEARNING TIPS

A **bar graph** uses vertical or horizontal bars to show data.

1. What does the **bar graph** show?

_____

_____

_____

How many students like broccoli best?

_____

What is the favourite vegetable in Rhea's class?

_____

How many students voted for their favourite vegetable?

_____

2. Chuck says the graph shows that nobody likes asparagus. Do you agree with him? Explain.

_____

_____

_____

Communicating about Probability

1. (Circle) the best word to describe each event.

A pig will fly.

impossible   unlikely   likely   certain

There will be 12 months this year.

impossible   unlikely   likely   certain

You will eat dessert at least once this week.

impossible   unlikely   likely   certain

You will see a rainbow this week.

impossible   unlikely   likely   certain

LEARNING TIPS

Although "likely" means more probable and "unlikely" means less probable, both likely and unlikely events can occur. Equally likely events have the same chance of happening.

2. (Circle) the more likely event.

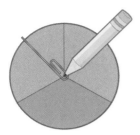

The spinner will land on green.

The spinner will land on purple.

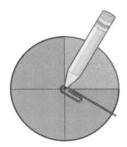

The spinner will land on blue.

The spinner will land on red.

3. Describe an event for each probability.

One event is more likely than the other.

_____

_____

One event is less likely than the other.

_____

_____

Probability Experiments

1. If you toss a coin 30 times, do you think heads or tails will land face up more often? (Circle) your answer.

head   tails   about the same

Toss a coin 20 times. Use tally marks to record your results in a table.

Heads	Tails

What do you think would happen if you tossed a coin with a different value 50 times?

_____

_____

_____

LEARNING TIPS

An experiment can help to determine the probability of an event.

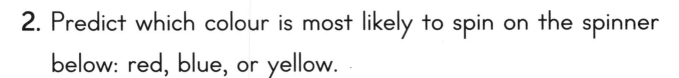

2. Predict which colour is most likely to spin on the spinner below: red, blue, or yellow.

_____

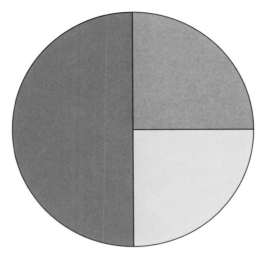

Use a pencil and a paper clip. Spin the spinner above 20 times. Use tally marks to record your results.

Red	Blue	Yellow

How do your results compare with your prediction?

_____

_____

Test Yourself

1. Look at the pictograph. Answer the questions below.

Number of Books Read in Our Class this Week

Each 📖 represents 1 book.

On which day were the most books read?

_____

On which days were the fewest books read?

_____

How many books were read altogether?

_____

2. Circle the best word to describe each event.

You will see a black car today.

impossible   unlikely   likely   certain

You will see a hot air balloon today.

impossible   unlikely   likely   certain

You will see a real-life unicorn today.

impossible   unlikely   likely   certain

3. Circle the best word to describe each event.

David will choose a yellow ball without looking.

unlikely   certain   impossible

David will choose a red ball without looking.

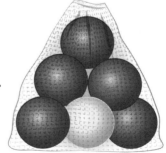

certain   likely   unlikely

David will choose a green ball without looking.

likely   unlikely   impossible

Glossary

Area: the amount of space covered by something.

Bar graph: a graph that uses vertical or horizontal bars to show data.

Capacity: describes how much liquid a container can hold.

Centimetre: a unit of measure. The symbol for a centimetre is cm. 100 cm = 1 m.

Divide: to separate into equal groups or shares.

Double: when a number is added to itself, it's called a double.

Edge: the line that joins two vertices on a 3-D object.

Face: a side or surface of a 3-D object.

Fact family: a group of math facts or related number sentences. Each fact uses the same numbers.

Fraction: a part of a whole.

Growing pattern: a pattern that increases in a regular way. Some growing patterns change by adding the same number over and over.

Line of symmetry: an imaginary line that divides a figure into 2 equal parts.

Metre: a unit of measurement that is longer than a centimetre. The symbol for metres is m. 1 m = 100 cm.

Multiply: to join equal groups.

Pattern core: the part of a pattern that repeats.

Pattern rule: a pattern rule describes how a pattern continues or repeats.

Perimeter: the distance around a shape or an object.

Pictograph: a graph with symbols to show information. The symbol is the same in each column or row.

Prism: a 3-D object with rectangular sides. The top and bottom can be rectangles, triangles, or another straight-sided shape.

Pyramid: a 3-D object with triangle sides that come together at a point. The bottom can be a square, a triangle, or another straight-sided shape.

Quadrilateral: a shape with 4 sides.

Regroup: to show the same number in a different way.

Shrinking pattern: a pattern that decreases, or shrinks, in a regular way.

Skeleton: a 3-D frame that shows the edges and vertices of a 3-D object.

Survey: a question asked to find information.

Tally marks: a way of keeping count by drawing marks.

Thermometer: a tool that tells temperature. When the temperature gets hotter, the red liquid goes up. When it gets colder, the liquid goes down.

Vertices (singular: **vertex**): the corners or points where the sides of a shape meet.

Answers

Reading and Writing Numbers

1. Match each number to its word.

13 — thirteen
4 — four
20 — twenty
0 — zero

(13→four, 4→thirteen, 20→twenty, 0→zero)

2. Write each word as a number.

three __3__   fifteen __15__

seven __7__   eighteen __18__

3. Write each number as a word.

11 __eleven__
14 __fourteen__
10 __ten__
12 __twelve__

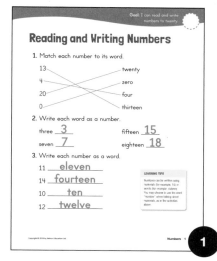

1

Counting Forward

1. Count forward on the 100-chart. Fill in the missing numbers.

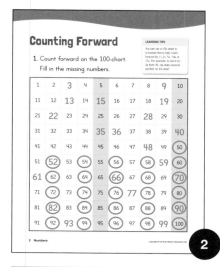

2

2. Use the 100-chart from Question 1. Start at 50 and count forward by 2s. Circle each number in your counting pattern.

Now, start at 5. Count forward by 5s. Colour each number in your counting pattern yellow.

3. Write the missing numbers on the number lines.

30 40 50 __60__ 70 __80__ __90__ 100

40 42 __44__ 46 48 __50__ 52 __54__

4. Write the missing numbers.

82, 83, 84, __85__, 86, __87__, __88__

34, 36, 38, __40__, __42__, 44, __46__

60, 65, 70, __75__, 80, __85__, __90__

19, 21, 23, __25__, __27__, 29, __31__

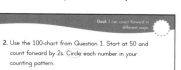

3

Counting Backward

1. Start at 100. Count backward on the 100-chart. Fill in the missing numbers.

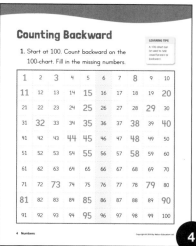

4

2. Write the missing numbers.

19, 18, 17, __16__, 15, __14__, __13__

40, 39, __38__, __37__, 36, __35__, 34

100, 90, __80__, __70__, 60, __50__, 40

3. Use the 100-chart from Question 1. Start at 96. Colour it red. Count backward by 10. Colour the square red. Continue to count backward by 10s. Colour the squares red.

What pattern do you notice?

__A column is coloured red in the__
__100-chart.__

4. Use the pattern you found in Question 3. Count backward by 10s from 91. Write the numbers.

__91, 81, 71, 61, 51, 41, 31, 21, 11, 1__

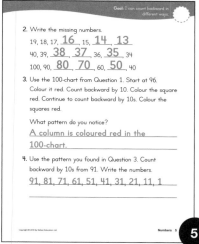

5

Representing Numbers

1. Circle groups of 10 buttons.

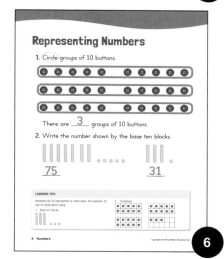

There are __3__ groups of 10 buttons.

2. Write the number shown by the base ten blocks.

__75__   __31__

6

3. Write the number shown in each set of 10-frames.

__24__

__16__

4. Draw dots on the 10-frames to represent each number.

28

47

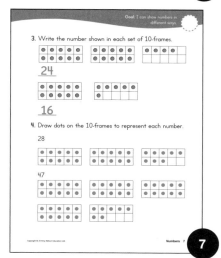

7

Renaming Numbers

1. Write the number of tens and the number of ones.

94 = __9__ tens and __4__ ones

28 = __2__ tens and __8__ ones

2. Write the number.

7 tens and 6 ones = __76__

3 tens and 9 ones = __39__

2 tens and 4 ones = __24__

3. Look at the base ten blocks. Write the number in two ways.

__2__ tens and __0__ ones = __20__

__1__ tens and __10__ ones = __20__

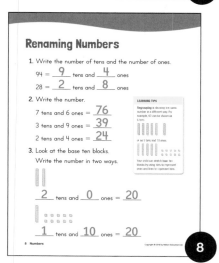

8

4. Write the number for each group of base ten blocks.

__40__

__84__

* 5. Write the number for each group of base ten blocks. Regroup the blocks. Draw a different set of base ten blocks to represent the same number.

__47__

__63__

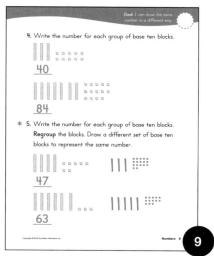

9

Comparing and Ordering Numbers

1. Circle the number that is greater. To help you, draw base ten blocks.

32 (41) |||| .. |||| .

(52) 29 |||| .. || ::::

14 (19) | .... | ::::

2. Circle the number that is less. To help you, draw base ten blocks.

48 (42) |||| ::: |||| .

32 39 ||| .. || :::

(71) 77 |||||||| ||||||| :::

10 Numbers

Copyright © 2018 by Nelson Education Ltd.

10

3. Mark each pair of numbers on the number line. Circle the number that is greater.

25 (33)

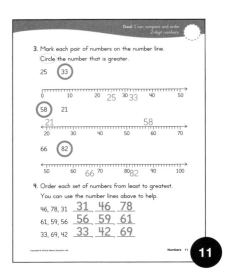

(58) 21

66 (82)

4. Order each set of numbers from least to greatest. You can use the number lines above to help.

46, 78, 31 __31_ , _46_ , _78_

61, 59, 56 __56_ , _59_ , _61_

33, 69, 42 __33_ , _42_ , _69_

Numbers 11

11

Rounding 2-Digit Numbers

1. Look at the blue number. Circle the nearest ten.

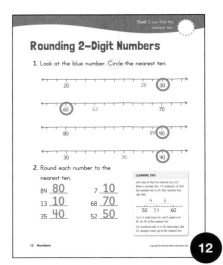

2. Round each number to the nearest ten.

84 _80_   7 _10_

13 _10_   68 _70_

35 _40_   52 _50_

12 Numbers

Copyright © 2018 by Nelson Education Ltd.

12

Counting Money

1. Name and write the value for each coin.

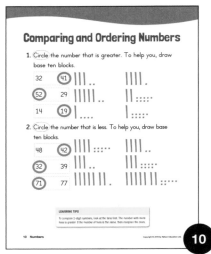

nickel _5_ ¢   dime _10_ ¢

quarter _25_ ¢   loonie $ _1_

toonie $ _2_

2. Write the total value of the coins.

_30_ ¢

_60_ ¢

Copyright © 2018 by Nelson Education Ltd.

Numbers 13

13

Representing Fractions

1. Colour one half of each shape.

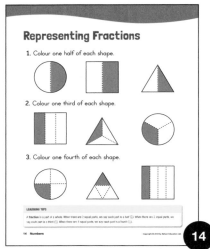

2. Colour one third of each shape.

3. Colour one fourth of each shape.

14 Numbers

Copyright © 2018 by Nelson Education Ltd.

14

4. Circle the shape that shows one half coloured.

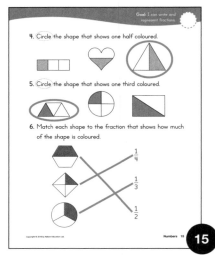

5. Circle the shape that shows one third coloured.

6. Match each shape to the fraction that shows how much of the shape is coloured.

$\frac{1}{4}$

$\frac{1}{3}$

$\frac{1}{2}$

Numbers 15

15

Comparing Fractions

1. Circle the fraction that shows how much of each shape is coloured.

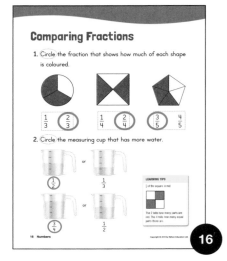

$\frac{1}{3}$ ($\frac{2}{3}$) $\frac{1}{4}$ ($\frac{2}{4}$)   ($\frac{3}{5}$) $\frac{4}{5}$

2. Circle the measuring cup that has more water.

$\frac{1}{2}$ $\frac{1}{3}$

$\frac{3}{4}$ $\frac{1}{2}$

16 Numbers

16

3. Circle the pie that has more left over.

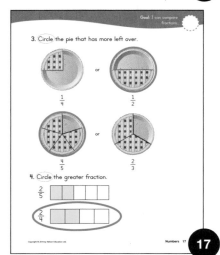

or

$\frac{1}{4}$ $\frac{1}{2}$

or

$\frac{4}{5}$ $\frac{2}{3}$

4. Circle the greater fraction.

$\frac{2}{5}$

($\frac{2}{4}$)

Numbers 17

17

Test Yourself

1. Write the number for each word.

eleven _11_   eighteen _18_

nine _9_   twelve _12_

2. Write the missing numbers.

12, 14, 16, _18_ , _20_ , 22, 24, _26_

25, 30, 35, _40_ , 45, _50_ , _55_ , 60

40, 39, 38, _37_ , 36, _35_ , _34_ , 33

3. Write the number shown by the base ten blocks.

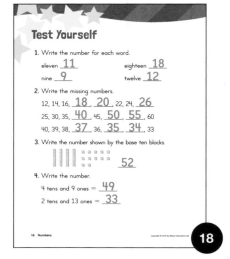

_52_

4. Write the number.

4 tens and 9 ones = _49_

2 tens and 13 ones = _33_

18 Numbers

Copyright © 2018 by Nelson Education Ltd.

18

* Sample answer provided.

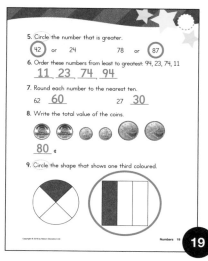

5. Circle the number that is greater.
(42) or 24   78 or (87)

6. Order these numbers from least to greatest: 94, 23, 74, 11
11 23 74 94

7. Round each number to the nearest ten.
62 60   27 30

8. Write the total value of the coins.
80 ¢

9. Circle the shape that shows one third coloured.

Numbers 19 **19**

Addition Strategies

1. Use counters on the 10-frames to add.

7 + 4 = 11   9 + 8 = 17
8 + 5 = 13   5 + 7 = 12
8 + 6 = 14   7 + 8 = 15
6 + 7 = 13   3 + 9 = 12

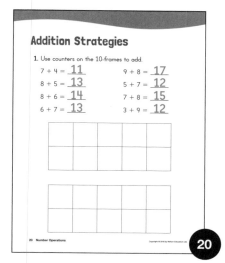

20 Number Operations **20**

Goal: I can make 10 and use doubles to help me add.

2. Add.
1 + 1 = 2   5 + 5 = 10
3 + 3 = 6   6 + 6 = 12
7 + 7 = 14   4 + 4 = 8
9 + 9 = 18   8 + 8 = 16

3. Add. Use **doubles** to help you.
3 + 2 = 5   2 + 1 = 3
4 + 5 = 9   6 + 7 = 13
4 + 3 = 7   8 + 9 = 17
8 + 7 = 15   6 + 5 = 11

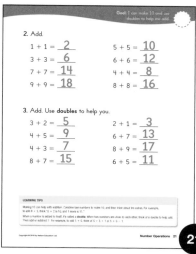

Number Operations 21 **21**

Goal: I can reorder numbers to help me add.

Reordering Numbers to Add

1. Complete each addition sentence.
3 + 1 = 4, so 1 + 3 = 4
4 + 5 = 9, so 5 + 4 = 9
2 + 4 = 6, so 4 + 2 = 6

2. Change the order of the numbers to help you add them. Then add.
9 + 5 + 1 = 9 + 1 + 5
= 10 + 5
= 15
5 + 3 + 5 = 5 + 5 + 3
= 10 + 3
= 13
8 + 7 + 2 = 8 + 2 + 7
= 10 + 7
= 17

22 Number Operations **22**

Goal: I can use mental math strategies to subtract.

Subtraction Strategies

1. Subtract. Think about a number line to help you.
5 − 2 = 3   12 − 9 = 3
8 − 4 = 4   18 − 14 = 4
9 − 3 = 6   15 − 11 = 4

2. Subtract. Think about addition to help you.
15 − 8 = 7   8 − 3 = 5
12 − 6 = 6   18 − 9 = 9
10 − 4 = 6   11 − 5 = 6

3. Subtract.
8 − 7 = 1   6 − 5 = 1
9 − 9 = 0   6 − 6 = 0
5 − 4 = 1   9 − 8 = 1

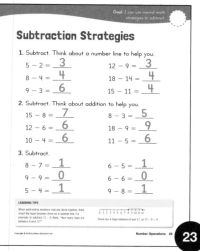

Number Operations 23 **23**

Goal: I can add and subtract with zero.

Exploring Zero

1. How many balls are there altogether?

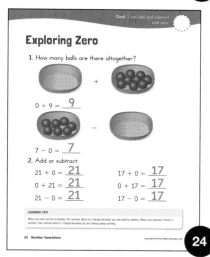

0 + 9 = 9

7 − 0 = 7

2. Add or subtract.
21 + 0 = 21   17 + 0 = 17
0 + 21 = 21   0 + 17 = 17
21 − 0 = 21   17 − 0 = 17

24 Number Operations **24**

Goal: I can add or subtract to solve problems.

Comparison Problems

Write an addition or a subtraction sentence for each question.

* 1. How many more green balls are there than orange balls?

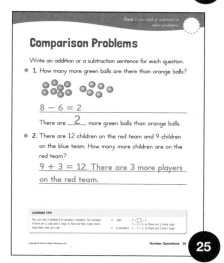

8 − 6 = 2

There are 2 more green balls than orange balls.

* 2. There are 12 children on the red team and 9 children on the blue team. How many more children are on the red team?

9 + 3 = 12. There are 3 more players on the red team.

Number Operations 25 **25**

Goal: I can make fact families.

Fact Families

* Make a **fact family** for each number.

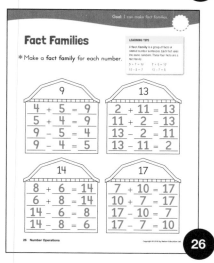

9
4 + 5 = 9
5 + 4 = 9
9 − 5 = 4
9 − 4 = 5

13
2 + 11 = 13
11 + 2 = 13
13 − 2 = 11
13 − 11 = 2

14
8 + 6 = 14
6 + 8 = 14
14 − 6 = 8
14 − 8 = 6

17
7 + 10 = 17
10 + 7 = 17
17 − 10 = 7
17 − 7 = 10

26 Number Operations **26**

Goal: I can solve math problems that have missing parts.

Missing−Part Addition and Subtraction

1. Balance each scale. Add or cross out balls on the left side. Then complete the addition or subtraction sentence.

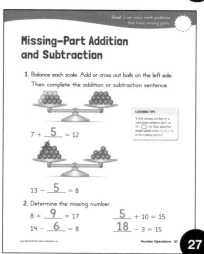

7 + 5 = 12

13 − 5 = 8

2. Determine the missing number.
8 + 9 = 17   5 + 10 = 15
14 − 6 = 8   18 − 3 = 15

Number Operations 27 **27**

* Sample answer provided.

Relating Equal Groups

✱ 1. Balance each scale. Draw linking cubes on one side.

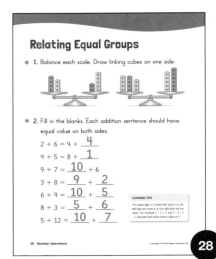

✱ 2. Fill in the blanks. Each addition sentence should have equal value on both sides.

$2 + 6 = 4 + \underline{4}$

$4 + 5 = 8 + \underline{1}$

$9 + 7 = \underline{10} + 6$

$3 + 8 = \underline{9} + \underline{2}$

$6 + 9 = \underline{10} + \underline{5}$

$8 + 3 = \underline{5} + \underline{6}$

$5 + 12 = \underline{10} + \underline{7}$

28

---

3. If the two sides are equal, write an equal sign in the box. If they are not equal, cross out the box.

$7 + 9 \;\boxed{=}\; 6 + 10$

$5 + 5 \;\boxed{\times}\; 6 + 3$

$11 + 6 \;\boxed{=}\; 8 + 9$

$3 + 12 \;\boxed{\times}\; 6 + 8$

$13 + 5 \;\boxed{=}\; 9 + 9$

✱ 4. Write 2 different addition expressions that equal the number given.

$10 = \underline{5} + \underline{5} = \underline{6} + \underline{4}$

$12 = \underline{6} + \underline{6} = \underline{11} + \underline{1}$

$9 = \underline{4} + \underline{5} = \underline{7} + \underline{2}$

$14 = \underline{10} + \underline{4} = \underline{12} + \underline{2}$

$16 = \underline{14} + \underline{2} = \underline{10} + \underline{6}$

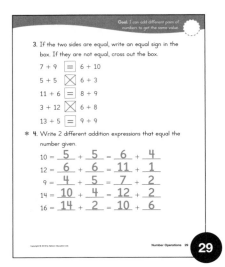

29

Adding 2-Digit Numbers

1. Add.

$20 + 20 = \underline{40}$ $20 + 40 = \underline{60}$

$30 + 50 = \underline{80}$ $80 + 20 = \underline{100}$

$40 + 30 = \underline{70}$ $30 + 10 = \underline{40}$

2. Add.

$35 + 10 = \underline{45}$ $44 + 10 = \underline{54}$

$18 + 10 = \underline{28}$ $67 + 10 = \underline{77}$

$22 + 10 = \underline{32}$ $56 + 10 = \underline{66}$

3. Separate the tens and ones for each number.

$22 = 20 + \underline{2}$ $34 = 30 + \underline{4}$

$76 = \underline{70} + 6$ $81 = \underline{80} + 1$

$55 = 50 + \underline{5}$ $99 = \underline{90} + 9$

30

---

4. Add by separating out the tens and ones for both numbers.

$26 + 11$ $43 + 35$

$20 + 10 = 30$ $40 + 30 = 70$

$6 + 1 = 7$ $3 + 5 = 8$

$30 + 7 = 37$ $70 + 8 = 78$

5. Add. Draw base ten blocks in the place-value chart to help you.

$22 + 56$

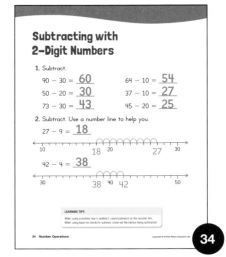

$\begin{array}{r} 2\,2 \\ +\ 5\,6 \\ \hline 7\,8 \end{array}$

31

Adding with Regrouping

1. Regroup to add.

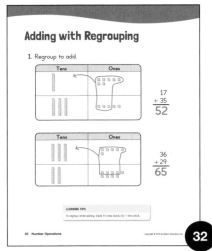

$\begin{array}{r} 17 \\ +\ 35 \\ \hline 52 \end{array}$

$\begin{array}{r} 36 \\ +\ 29 \\ \hline 65 \end{array}$

32

---

2. Show how to add 44 + 28. Draw base ten blocks on the place value chart. Then add.

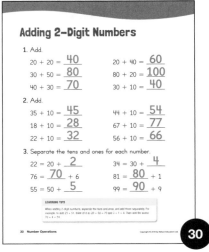

$\begin{array}{r} 4\,4 \\ +\ 2\,8 \\ \hline 7\,2 \end{array}$

3. Regroup to add.

$\begin{array}{r} 66 \\ +\ 18 \\ \hline 84 \end{array}$ $\begin{array}{r} 28 \\ +\ 38 \\ \hline 66 \end{array}$ $\begin{array}{r} 26 \\ +\ 14 \\ \hline 40 \end{array}$

$\begin{array}{r} 64 \\ +\ 27 \\ \hline 91 \end{array}$ $\begin{array}{r} 34 \\ +\ 59 \\ \hline 93 \end{array}$ $\begin{array}{r} 25 \\ +\ 47 \\ \hline 72 \end{array}$

33

Subtracting with 2-Digit Numbers

1. Subtract.

$90 - 30 = \underline{60}$ $64 - 10 = \underline{54}$

$50 - 20 = \underline{30}$ $37 - 10 = \underline{27}$

$73 - 30 = \underline{43}$ $45 - 20 = \underline{25}$

2. Subtract. Use a number line to help you.

$27 - 9 = \underline{18}$

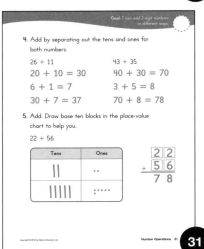

$42 - 4 = \underline{38}$

34

---

3. Subtract. Cross out the blocks that are being subtracted.

$45 - 23 = \underline{22}$

$68 - 35 = \underline{33}$

$77 - 32 = \underline{45}$

4. Subtract. Draw base ten blocks to help you.

$44 - 13 = \underline{31}$ $25 - 15 = \underline{10}$

$56 - 32 = \underline{24}$ $99 - 18 = \underline{81}$

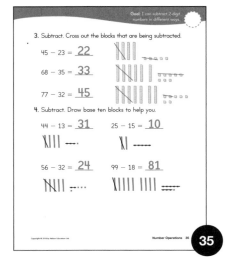

35

Subtracting with Regrouping

1. Subtract. Regroup 1 ten for 10 ones. Use the place value charts to help you.

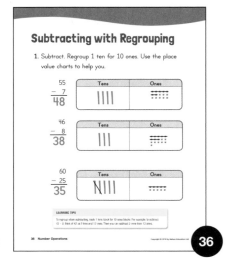

$\begin{array}{r} 55 \\ -\ 7 \\ \hline 48 \end{array}$

$\begin{array}{r} 46 \\ -\ 8 \\ \hline 38 \end{array}$

$\begin{array}{r} 60 \\ -\ 25 \\ \hline 35 \end{array}$

36

✱ Sample answer provided.

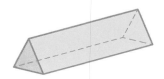

Page 37

2. Subtract by regrouping.

```
  65        5 tens   15 ones
 - 7      -          7 ones
 ----      -------   --------
  58        5 tens    8 ones
```

```
  43        3 tens   13 ones
 - 6      -          6 ones
 ----      -------   --------
  37        3 tens    7 ones
```

3. Subtract.

```
  42       51       64
 - 13     - 33     - 28
 ----     ----     ----
  29       18       36
```

```
  23       72       45
 - 18     - 44     - 26
 ----     ----     ----
   5       28       19
```

Page 38

Adding and Subtracting with Money

1. Is there enough money to buy each item? Write how much money there is. Circle the answer.

LEARNING TIPS
Because pennies are not used in Canada anymore, purchases made with cash are rounded to the nearest 5 cents.

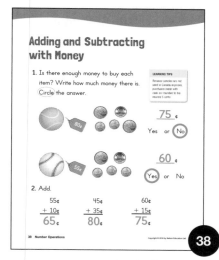

75¢
Yes or (No)

60¢
(Yes) or No

2. Add.

```
  55¢      45¢      60¢
 + 10¢    + 35¢    + 15¢
 -----    -----    -----
  65¢      80¢      75¢
```

Page 39

3. Subtract.

```
  50¢      85¢      45¢
 - 35¢    - 30¢    - 25¢
 -----    -----    -----
  15¢      55¢      20¢
```

* 4. Circle two items you can buy together if you have 75¢. Show your addition.

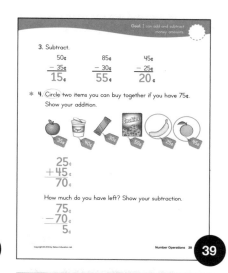

```
  25¢
 + 45¢
 -----
  70¢
```

How much do you have left? Show your subtraction.

```
  75¢
 - 70¢
 -----
   5¢
```

Page 40

Exploring Multiplication

1. Write an addition sentence for each picture. Then write a multiplication sentence.

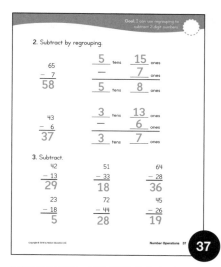

__2__ + __2__ + __2__ = __6__
__3__ groups of __2__ butterflies
__3__ × __2__ = __6__

__5__ + __5__ = __10__
__2__ groups of __5__ ladybugs
__2__ × __5__ = __10__

LEARNING TIPS
You multiply when you join equal groups. For example, 2 + 2 + 2 can be written as 4 × 2. This means the total of 4 groups of 2. So, 4 × 2 = 8.

Page 41

2. Write each addition sentence as a multiplication sentence. Then multiply.

3 + 3 + 3 + 3 + 3 = __15__
__5__ × __3__ = __15__

4 + 4 = __8__
__2__ × __4__ = __8__

2 + 2 + 2 + 2 = __8__
__4__ × __2__ = __8__

3. Multiply. Draw a picture to help you.

2 × 2 = __4__

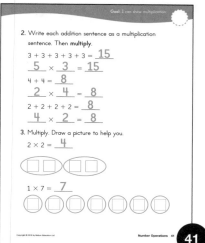

1 × 7 = __7__

Page 42

Exploring Division

LEARNING TIPS
To divide means to separate a collection into equal groups or shares. For example, to share 6 stickers between 2 people, each person gets 3 stickers.

1. You have 8 jelly beans for 2 people to share. Show how you can share the jelly beans equally.

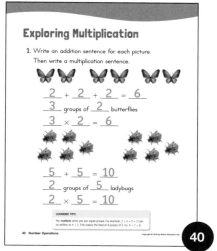

Complete the division sentence: 8 ÷ 2 = __4__
Each person gets __4__ jelly beans.

2. You have 6 pears for 3 people to share. Show how you can share the pears equally.

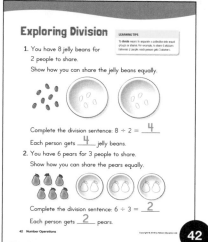

Complete the division sentence: 6 ÷ 3 = __2__
Each person gets __2__ pears.

* Sample answer provided.

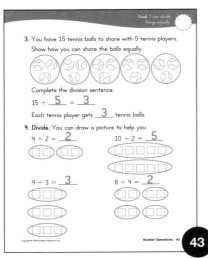

3. You have 15 tennis balls to share with 5 tennis players. Show how you can share the balls equally.

Complete the division sentence.

15 ÷ __5__ = __3__

Each tennis player gets __3__ tennis balls.

4. **Divide.** You can draw a picture to help you.

4 ÷ 2 = __2__   10 ÷ 2 = __5__

9 ÷ 3 = __3__   8 ÷ 4 = __2__

Number Operations 43

43

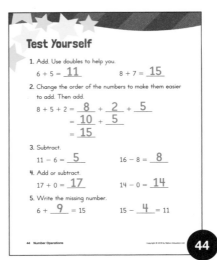

Test Yourself

1. Add. Use doubles to help you.

6 + 5 = __11__   8 + 7 = __15__

2. Change the order of the numbers to make them easier to add. Then add.

8 + 5 + 2 = __8__ + __2__ + __5__
= __10__ + __5__
= __15__

3. Subtract.

11 − 6 = __5__   16 − 8 = __8__

4. Add or subtract.

17 + 0 = __17__   14 − 0 = __14__

5. Write the missing number.

6 + __9__ = 15   15 − __4__ = 11

44 Number Operations

44

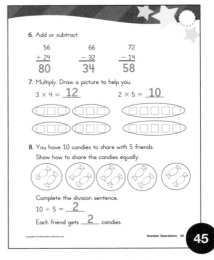

6. Add or subtract.

```
  56        66        72
+ 24      − 32      − 14
  80        34        58
```

7. Multiply. Draw a picture to help you.

3 × 4 = __12__   2 × 5 = __10__

8. You have 10 candies to share with 5 friends. Show how to share the candies equally.

Complete the division sentence.

10 ÷ 5 = __2__

Each friend gets __2__ candies.

Number Operations 45

45

Measuring in Centimetres

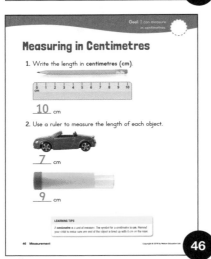

1. Write the length in centimetres (cm).

__10__ cm

2. Use a ruler to measure the length of each object.

__7__ cm

__9__ cm

LEARNING TIPS

A **centimetre** is a unit of measure. The symbol for a centimetre is cm. Remind your child to make sure one end of the object is lined up with 0 cm on the ruler.

46 Measurement

46

Measuring in Metres

* 1. Use a measuring tape to measure each object to the nearest **metre (m)**.

the length of your bed: about __2__ m

the length of a table: about __2__ m

the length of a wall: about __4__ m

the length of a hallway: about __3__ m

2. Circle the most appropriate unit of measurement for each object.

the length of your school

cm   (m)

the length of your finger

(cm)   m

the length of a school bus

cm   (m)

LEARNING TIPS

A **metre** is a unit of measurement that is longer than a centimetre. The symbol for metres is m. 1 m = 100 cm

If you do not have a metre stick or measuring tape in your home, your child can estimate distances/measurements in metres.

Measurement 47

47

Using Benchmarks to Estimate

* 1. Estimate the length in centimetres. Then use a ruler to measure.

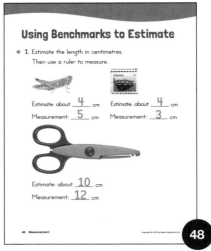

Estimate: about __4__ cm   Estimate: about __4__ cm

Measurement: __5__ cm   Measurement: __3__ cm

Estimate: about __10__ cm

Measurement: __12__ cm

48 Measurement

48

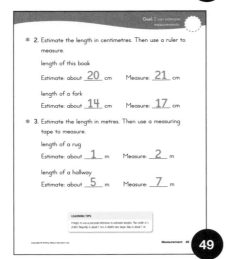

* 2. Estimate the length in centimetres. Then use a ruler to measure.

length of this book

Estimate: about __20__ cm   Measure: __21__ cm

length of a fork

Estimate: about __14__ cm   Measure: __17__ cm

* 3. Estimate the length in metres. Then use a measuring tape to measure.

length of a rug

Estimate: about __1__ m   Measure: __2__ m

length of a hallway

Estimate: about __5__ m   Measure: __7__ m

LEARNING TIPS

It helps to use a personal reference to estimate lengths. The width of a child's fingertip is about 1 cm. A child's very large step is about 1 m.

Measurement 49

49

Measuring Perimeter

1. Find the **perimeter** of each object.

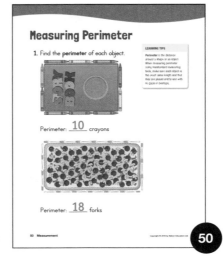

LEARNING TIPS

Perimeter is the distance around a shape or an object. When measuring perimeter using nonstandard measuring tools, make sure each object is the exact same length and that they are placed end to end with no gaps or overlaps.

Perimeter: __10__ crayons

Perimeter: __18__ forks

50 Measurement

50

---

2. Place a separate piece of string along the perimeter of each shape. Start the string at the star. Cut each piece of string to match the perimeter of the shape.

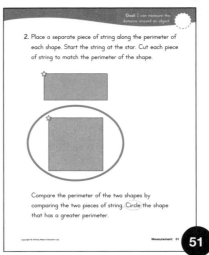

Compare the perimeter of the two shapes by comparing the two pieces of string. Circle the shape that has a greater perimeter.

Measurement 51

51

---

* Sample answer provided.

Days, Weeks, Months, and Years

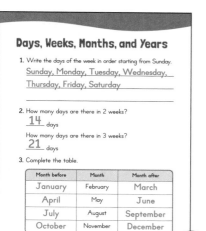

1. Write the days of the week in order starting from Sunday.
   Sunday, Monday, Tuesday, Wednesday, Thursday, Friday, Saturday

2. How many days are there in 2 weeks?
   __14__ days
   How many days are there in 3 weeks?
   __21__ days

3. Complete the table.

Month before	Month	Month after
January	February	March
April	May	June
July	August	September
October	November	December

52 Measurement

52

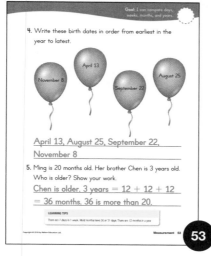

4. Write these birth dates in order from earliest in the year to latest.

(balloons: November 8, April 13, September 22, August 25)

April 13, August 25, September 22, November 8

5. Ming is 20 months old. Her brother Chen is 3 years old. Who is older? Show your work.
   Chen is older. 3 years = 12 + 12 + 12 = 36 months. 36 is more than 20.

LEARNING TIPS
There are 7 days in 1 week. Most months have 30 or 31 days. There are 12 months in a year.

Measurement 53

53

Telling Time

1. Write each time using words.

quarter past five   half past six   quarter past one

2. Draw hands on the clock to show each time.
   three o'clock   half past two   quarter to seven

LEARNING TIPS
Remind your child that the big hand shows minutes and the small hand shows hours. Help your child to think of time in quarters of an hour. For example, a quarter past means 15 minutes past a certain hour.

54 Measurement

54

---

3. Match each clock to the correct time.

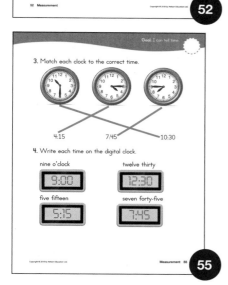

4:15   7:45   10:30

4. Write each time on the digital clock.
   nine o'clock   9:00
   twelve thirty   12:30
   five fifteen   5:15
   seven forty-five   7:45

Measurement 55

55

Understanding Temperature

1. Circle the **thermometer** in each pair that shows a colder temperature.

2. The thermometer on the left shows the temperature in the morning. In the afternoon it gets warmer. Colour the thermometer to show what it might look like.

morning   afternoon

LEARNING TIPS
A thermometer tells temperature. When the temperature gets hotter, the red liquid goes up. When it gets colder, the liquid goes down.

56 Measurement

56

---

3. Draw a circle around each item of clothing people might wear if the thermometer looks like this.

Measurement 57

57

Test Yourself

1. Circle the most appropriate unit of measurement for each object.
   the height of a flag pole   cm   (m)
   the length of a book   (cm)   m

* 2. Estimate the length of each object in centimetres. Then measure to check your estimate.
   Estimate: about __5__ cm
   Measurement: __6__ cm
   Estimate: about __4__ cm
   Measurement: __5__ cm

3. Leah is 36 months old. Her brother Lucas is 2 years old. Who is older? Show your work.
   Leah is older. 2 years = 12 + 12 = 24 months. 36 is more than 24.

58 Measurement

58

---

4. Find the perimeter of the picture frame.

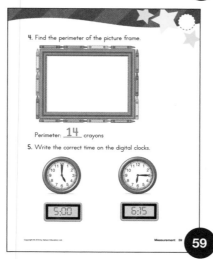

Perimeter: __14__ crayons

5. Write the correct time on the digital clocks.

5:00   6:15

Measurement 59

59

Identifying 2-D Shapes

1. Write the number of sides and number of **vertices** for each shape.

LEARNING TIPS
Vertices (singular: vertex) are the points or corners where the sides of a shape meet.

Shape	Number of sides	Number of vertices
triangle	3	3
rectangle	4	4
square	4	4
pentagon	5	5
hexagon	6	6
octagon	8	8

60 2-D Geometry

60

---

* Sample answer provided.

2. A quadrilateral has 4 sides. Circle the quadrilaterals.

3. Match each street sign with its shape name.

octagon   pentagon   quadrilateral

61

Sorting 2-D Shapes

1. Colour the triangles red, the quadrilaterals blue, the pentagons orange, the hexagons green, and the octagons purple.

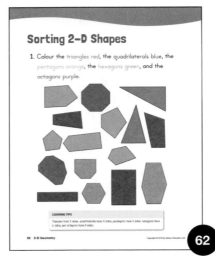

LEARNING TIPS
Triangles have 3 sides, quadrilaterals have 4 sides, pentagons have 5 sides, hexagons have 6 sides, and octagons have 8 sides.

62

2. Circle the shapes with 4 or fewer vertices. Underline the shapes with 5 or more vertices.

triangle   pentagon   rectangle

hexagon   square   octagon

Draw these shapes on the correct grid.

Shapes with 4 or fewer vertices

Shapes with 5 or more vertices

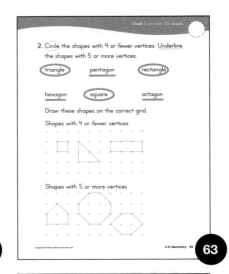

63

Pictures Using 2-D Shapes

1. Name the shapes in this picture. How many of each shape are there?

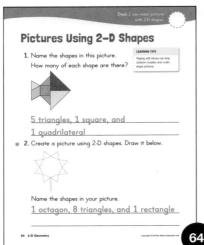

5 triangles, 1 square, and
1 quadrilateral

✶ 2. Create a picture using 2-D shapes. Draw it below.

Name the shapes in your picture.
1 octagon, 8 triangles, and 1 rectangle

64

Creating and Taking Apart 2-D Shapes

✶ 1. Create a square by drawing 2 triangles.

LEARNING TIPS
You can often find smaller shapes inside larger shapes. For example, this square is divided into 4 smaller triangles, 1 large triangle, and 1 quadrilateral.

Create a rectangle by drawing 2 triangles.

✶ 2. Take apart the rectangles. Draw lines on each rectangle to make 4 new shapes.

65

Exploring Symmetry

1. Circle each shape that shows one line of symmetry.

2. Draw at least one line of symmetry on each shape.

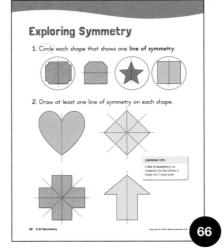

LEARNING TIPS
A line of symmetry is an imaginary line that divides a shape into 2 equal parts.

66

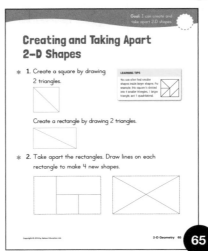

✶ Sample answer provided.

110 Answers

Copyright © 2018 by Nelson Education Ltd.

3. Each dotted line is the line of symmetry. Draw the other half of each shape.

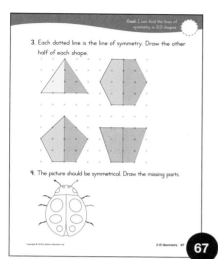

4. The picture should be symmetrical. Draw the missing parts.

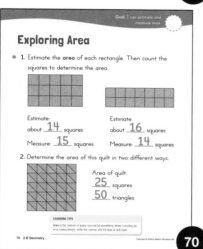

2-D Geometry 67

67

Objects on a Map

This is Eva's bedroom. Eva is standing in front of her bedroom door.

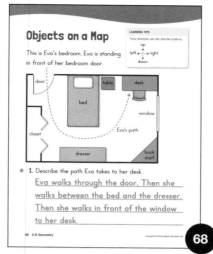

* 1. Describe the path Eva takes to her desk.

Eva walks through the door. Then she walks between the bed and the dresser. Then she walks in front of the window to her desk.

68 2-D Geometry

68

---

2. Circle the correct word to describe the positions of the objects in Eva's room.

The door is to the (left) / right of the bed

The desk is to the left / (right) of the table.

3. Draw a simple map of your own bedroom.

Answers will vary.

2-D Geometry 69

69

Exploring Area

* 1. Estimate the **area** of each rectangle. Then count the squares to determine the area.

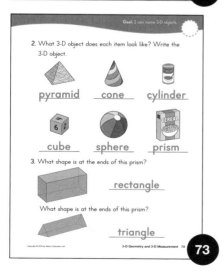

Estimate: about 14 squares   Estimate: about 16 squares

Measure: 15 squares   Measure: 14 squares

2. Determine the area of this quilt in two different ways.

Area of quilt:
25 squares
50 triangles

70 2-D Geometry

70

Test Yourself

1. Complete the table.

Shape	Draw the shape	Number of sides
square		4
triangle		3
rectangle		4

2. Draw at least one line of symmetry on each shape.

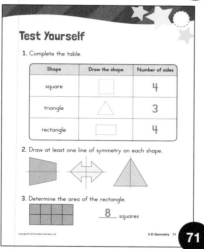

3. Determine the area of the rectangle.

8 squares

2-D Geometry 71

71

Identifying 3–D Objects

1. Match the 3-D object to its name.

cube
pyramid
sphere
prism
cone
cylinder

72 3-D Geometry and 3-D Measurement

72

---

2. What 3-D object does each item look like? Write the 3-D object.

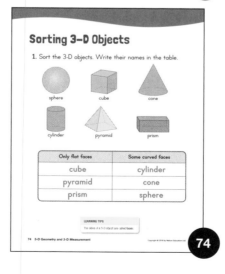

pyramid   cone   cylinder

cube   sphere   prism

3. What shape is at the ends of this prism?

rectangle

What shape is at the ends of this prism?

triangle

3-D Geometry and 3-D Measurement 73

73

Sorting 3–D Objects

1. Sort the 3-D objects. Write their names in the table.

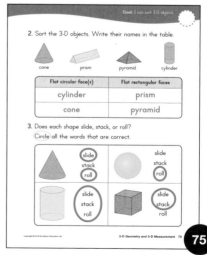

sphere   cube   cone

cylinder   pyramid   prism

Only flat faces	Some curved faces
cube	cylinder
pyramid	cone
prism	sphere

74 3-D Geometry and 3-D Measurement

74

---

2. Sort the 3-D objects. Write their names in the table.

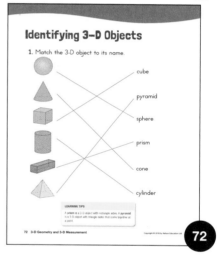

cone   prism   pyramid   cylinder

Flat circular face(s)	Flat rectangular faces
cylinder	prism
cone	pyramid

3. Does each shape slide, stack, or roll? Circle all the words that are correct.

(slide)   slide
stack   (stack)
(roll)   (roll)

slide   (slide)
(stack)   stack
roll   roll

3-D Geometry and 3-D Measurement 75

75

---

* Sample answer provided.

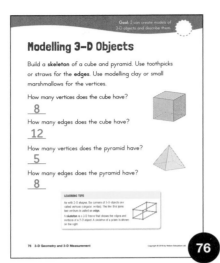

Modelling 3-D Objects

Build a **skeleton** of a cube and pyramid. Use toothpicks or straws for the **edges**. Use modelling clay or small marshmallows for the vertices.

How many vertices does the cube have?
_8_

How many edges does the cube have?
_12_

How many vertices does the pyramid have?
_5_

How many edges does the pyramid have?
_8_

LEARNING TIPS

As with 2-D shapes, the corners of 3-D objects are called vertices (singular: vertex). The line that joins two vertices is called an **edge**.

A **skeleton** is a 3-D frame that shows the edges and vertices of a 3-D object. A skeleton of a prism is shown on the right.

76 3-D Geometry and 3-D Measurement   Copyright © 2018 by Nelson Education Ltd.   **76**

Exploring Mass

1. Circle the heavier object.

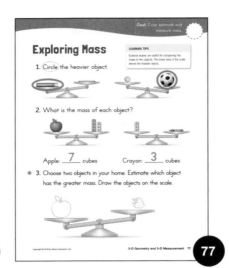

LEARNING TIPS

Balance scales are useful for comparing the mass of two objects. The lower side of the scale shows the heavier object.

2. What is the mass of each object?

Apple: _7_ cubes   Crayon: _3_ cubes

* 3. Choose two objects in your home. Estimate which object has the greater mass. Draw the objects on the scale.

77 3-D Geometry and 3-D Measurement   **77**

Exploring Capacity

1. Circle the container that has a greater **capacity**.

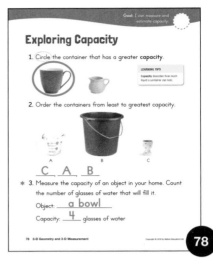

LEARNING TIPS

Capacity describes how much liquid a container can hold.

2. Order the containers from least to greatest capacity.

_C_ _A_ _B_

* 3. Measure the capacity of an object in your home. Count the number of glasses of water that will fill it.

Object: _a bowl_

Capacity: _4_ glasses of water

78 3-D Geometry and 3-D Measurement   Copyright © 2018 by Nelson Education Ltd.   **78**

Test Yourself

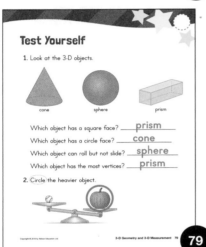

1. Look at the 3-D objects.

cone   sphere   prism

Which object has a square face? _prism_

Which object has a circle face? _cone_

Which object can roll but not slide? _sphere_

Which object has the most vertices? _prism_

2. Circle the heavier object.

Copyright © 2018 by Nelson Education Ltd.   3-D Geometry and 3-D Measurement 79   **79**

Repeating Patterns

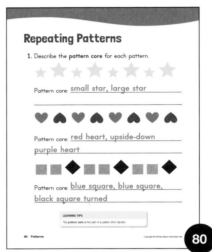

1. Describe the **pattern core** for each pattern.

Pattern core: _small star, large star_

Pattern core: _red heart, upside-down purple heart_

Pattern core: _blue square, blue square, black square turned_

LEARNING TIPS

The pattern core is the part of a pattern that repeats.

80 Patterns   Copyright © 2018 by Nelson Education Ltd.   **80**

2. Draw the missing picture for each pattern.

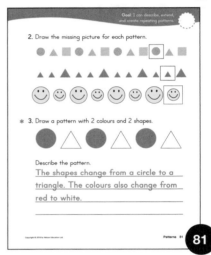

* 3. Draw a pattern with 2 colours and 2 shapes.

Describe the pattern.

The shapes change from a circle to a triangle. The colours also change from red to white.

Copyright © 2018 by Nelson Education Ltd.   Patterns 81   **81**

Growing Patterns

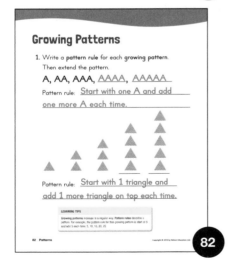

1. Write a **pattern rule** for each **growing pattern**. Then extend the pattern.

A, AA, AAA, _AAAA_, _AAAAA_

Pattern rule: _Start with one A and add one more A each time._

Pattern rule: _Start with 1 triangle and add 1 more triangle on top each time._

LEARNING TIPS

Growing patterns increase in a regular way. Pattern rules describe a pattern. For example, the pattern rule for this growing pattern is: start at 5 and add 5 each time: 5, 10, 15, 20, 25.

82 Patterns   Copyright © 2018 by Nelson Education Ltd.   **82**

2. Write the number you add for each growing pattern. Then extend the pattern.

20, 22, 24, 26, 28, _30_, _32_, _34_

Pattern rule: Add _2_ each time

35, 40, 45, 50, 55, _60_, _65_, _70_

Pattern rule: Add _5_ each time

3. Is this a growing pattern? Explain why or why not.
2, 4, 6, 8, 10

Yes, because you start at 2 and then add 2 each time.

Is this a growing pattern? Explain why or why not.
1, 2, 7, 10, 12

No, because you start at 1 and then add 1, then 5, then 3, then 2.

Patterns 83   **83**

Shrinking Patterns

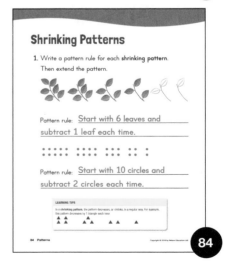

1. Write a pattern rule for each **shrinking pattern**. Then extend the pattern.

Pattern rule: _Start with 6 leaves and subtract 1 leaf each time._

Pattern rule: _Start with 10 circles and subtract 2 circles each time._

LEARNING TIPS

In a **shrinking pattern**, the pattern decreases, or shrinks, in a regular way. For example, this pattern decreases by 1 triangle each time.

84 Patterns   Copyright © 2018 by Nelson Education Ltd.   **84**

* Sample answer provided.

2. Write the number you subtract for each shrinking pattern. Then extend the pattern

19, 18, 17, 16, 15, __14__, __13__, __12__

Pattern rule: Subtract __1__ each time.

35, 30, 25, 20, 15, __10__, __5__, __0__

Pattern rule: Subtract __5__ each time.

3. Is this a shrinking pattern? Explain why or why not.

50, 40, 38, 20, 15

__No, because you start at 50 and then subtract 10, then 2, then 18, then 5.__

Is this a shrinking pattern? Explain why or why not.

20, 18, 16, 14, 12

__Yes, because you start at 20 and then subtract 2 each time.__

Patterns in a 100-Chart

LEARNING TIPS
Your child can use the words "column" and "row" to help describe the pattern. Remind your child to remove the counters before starting a new pattern.

You will need small objects, such as buttons or dimes, to use as counters on the 100-chart.

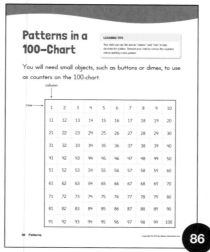

---

1. Place counters on the 100-chart to make each pattern. Describe how the counters look on the 100-chart.

Start at 5. Skip count forward by 5s to 50.

__There are straight vertical lines in the 5 and 10 columns.__

Start at 30. Skip count backward by 2s to 22.

__Every second number in the third row is covered.__

2. What pattern do you notice on the 100-chart when skip counting by 2s?

__Every second number is covered. The columns with numbers ending in 2, 4, 6, 8, and 0 are covered.__

Creating Patterns

★ **1.** Create a growing number pattern. Write the pattern rule.

__1__ __3__ __5__ __7__ __9__

Pattern rule: Add __2__ each time.

Create a shrinking number pattern. Write the pattern rule.

__100__ __90__ __80__ __70__ __60__

Pattern rule: Subtract __10__ each time.

2. Draw 1 nickel. Create a growing pattern using more nickels.

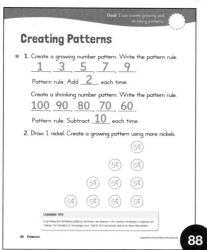

LEARNING TIPS
In growing and shrinking patterns, numbers can change or the number of shapes or objects can change. For Question 2, encourage your child to find and use actual nickels to show the pattern.

Test Yourself

1. Draw the missing picture for the pattern.

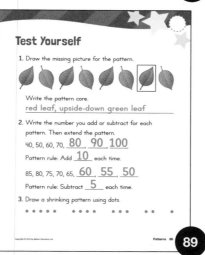

Write the pattern core.
__red leaf, upside-down green leaf__

2. Write the number you add or subtract for each pattern. Then extend the pattern.

40, 50, 60, 70, __80__, __90__, __100__

Pattern rule: Add __10__ each time.

85, 80, 75, 70, 65, __60__, __55__, __50__

Pattern rule: Subtract __5__ each time.

3. Draw a shrinking pattern using dots.

• • • • •   • • • •   • • •   • •   •

Organizing Objects

1. Write the name or draw a picture of each object in the correct box.

LEARNING TIPS
Tables are often helpful when organizing objects.

Conducting a Survey

★ Ask friends and family this **survey** question: What is your favourite day of the week? Use this tally chart to collect your data. Use one **tally mark** for each person's favourite.

Favourite day of the week	Tally
Sunday	II
Monday	
Tuesday	I
Wednesday	
Thursday	I
Friday	III
(Saturday)	IIII

Circle the favourite day.

LEARNING TIPS
A survey is a question asked to find information. A tally mark is a way of keeping count by drawing marks. This is how tally marks appear to represent each number.

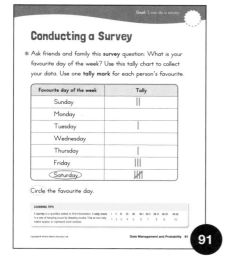

Pictographs

1. Look at the pictograph. Answer the questions below.

Favourite Colours in Lianne's Class

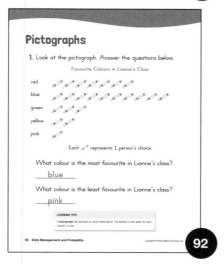

Each ✎ represents 1 person's choice.

What colour is the most favourite in Lianne's class?
__blue__

What colour is the least favourite in Lianne's class?
__pink__

LEARNING TIPS
A pictograph has symbols to show information. The symbol is the same in each column or row.

---

2. Use the data in the table below to create a pictograph.

Treats Sold at a Bake Sale	
cupcakes	5
cookies	7
brownies	3

Title: __Treats Sold at a Bake Sale__

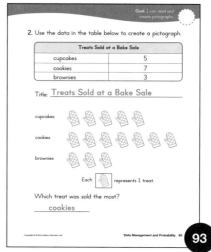

Each 🧤 represents 1 treat.

Which treat was sold the most?
__cookies__

★ Sample answer provided.

Bar Graphs

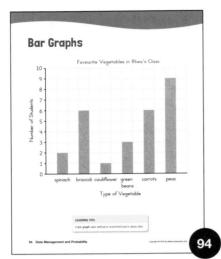

Favourite Vegetables in Rhea's Class

(Bar graph: Number of Students vs Type of Vegetable — spinach 2, broccoli 6, cauliflower 1, green beans 3, carrots 6, peas 9)

LEARNING TIPS
A bar graph uses vertical or horizontal bars to show data.

94 Data Management and Probability

---

1. What does the **bar graph** show?

<u>The graph shows the favourite vegetables</u>
<u>in Rhea's class and the number of people</u>
<u>that chose each of those vegetables.</u>

How many students like broccoli best?

<u>6</u>

What is the favourite vegetable in Rhea's class?

<u>peas</u>

How many students voted for their favourite vegetable?

<u>27</u>

2. Chuck says the graph shows that nobody likes asparagus. Do you agree with him? Explain.

<u>No, I don't agree because the graph</u>
<u>shows favourite vegetables. This means</u>
<u>that some people may like asparagus, but</u>
<u>it is not their favourite.</u>

Data Management and Probability 95

Communicating about Probability

1. Circle the best word to describe each event.

A pig will fly.

(impossible) unlikely likely certain

There will be 12 months this year.

impossible unlikely likely (certain)

You will eat dessert at least once this week.

impossible unlikely (likely) certain

You will see a rainbow this week.

impossible (unlikely) likely certain

LEARNING TIPS
Although "likely" means more probable and "unlikely" means less probable, both likely and unlikely events can occur. Equally likely events have the same chance of happening.

96 Data Management and Probability

---

2. Circle the more likely event.

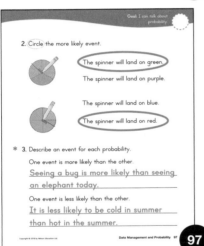

(The spinner will land on green.)

The spinner will land on purple.

The spinner will land on blue.

(The spinner will land on red.)

* 3. Describe an event for each probability.

One event is more likely than the other.

<u>Seeing a bug is more likely than seeing</u>
<u>an elephant today.</u>

One event is less likely than the other.

<u>It is less likely to be cold in summer</u>
<u>than hot in the summer.</u>

Data Management and Probability 97

Probability Experiments

* 1. If you toss a coin 30 times, do you think heads or tails will land face up more often? Circle your answer.

head tails (about the same)

Toss a coin 20 times. Use tally marks to record your results in a table.

Heads	Tails
Answers will vary.	Answers will vary.

What do you think would happen if you tossed a coin with a different value 50 times?

<u>The results would be similar. There are</u>
<u>still only two sides of a coin. Each side is</u>
<u>equally likely to land face up.</u>

LEARNING TIPS
An experiment can help to determine the probability of an event.

98 Data Management and Probability

---

2. Predict which colour is most likely to spin on the spinner below: red, blue, or yellow.

<u>red</u>

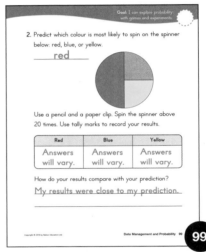

Use a pencil and a paper clip. Spin the spinner above 20 times. Use tally marks to record your results.

Red	Blue	Yellow
Answers will vary.	Answers will vary.	Answers will vary.

How do your results compare with your prediction?

<u>My results were close to my prediction.</u>

Data Management and Probability 99

Test Yourself

1. Look at the pictograph. Answer the questions below.

Number of Books Read in Our Class this Week

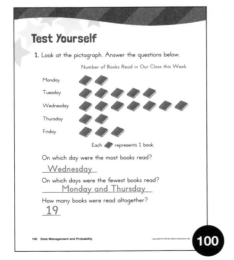

Each 📖 represents 1 book.

On which day were the most books read?

<u>Wednesday</u>

On which days were the fewest books read?

<u>Monday and Thursday</u>

How many books were read altogether?

<u>19</u>

100 Data Management and Probability

---

2. Circle the best word to describe each event.

You will see a black car today.

impossible unlikely (likely) certain

You will see a hot air balloon today.

impossible (unlikely) likely certain

You will see a real-life unicorn today.

(impossible) unlikely likely certain

3. Circle the best word to describe each event.

David will choose a yellow ball without looking.

(unlikely) certain impossible

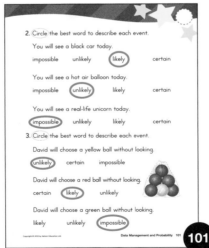

David will choose a red ball without looking.

certain (likely) unlikely

David will choose a green ball without looking.

likely unlikely (impossible)

Data Management and Probability 101

---

* Sample answer provided.

COMPLETION CERTIFICATE

CONGRATULATIONS!

You have completed the Nelson Math Grade 2 Workbook!

Presented to:

_____

Date:

_____

GREAT JOB!